MENSA
VISUAL
PUZZLES

THIS IS A CARLTON BOOK

Text and puzzle content copyright © British Mensa Limited 1997
Design and artwork copyright © Carlton Books Limited 1997

A CIP catalogue for this book is available from the British Library

ISBN 1-85868-324-6

Printed and bound in Italy

Puzzle Checker: David Ballheimer
Puzzle Design: Pauline Hoyle

MENSA
VISUAL
PUZZLES

Over 200 optical challenges to
test your powers of reasoning

John Bremner

CARLTON

Are you smart enough to join Mensa?

Solving puzzles can be a rewarding experience. The moment when you discover you have unravelled the puzzle compiler's convoluted logic is always brings a glow of satisfaction. But we thought you deserved something more. So Mensa are offering tangible proof of your mental prowess. Solve the following fiendishly difficult puzzles and we will send you a free certificate as proof of your achievement.

Puzzle 1
Which of these shapes is the odd one out?

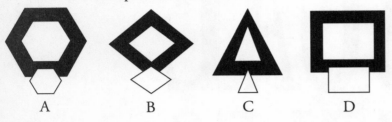

A   B   C   D

Puzzle 2
When the rope is pulled as shown, which container will the ball fall into, A or B?

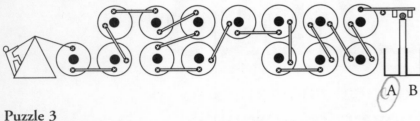

A B

Puzzle 3
Which two of these do not go with the other three?

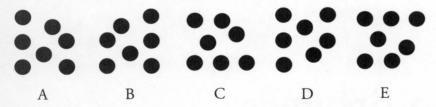

A   B   C   D   E

Puzzle 4
What comes next in these series?

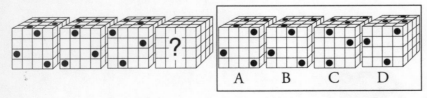

A   B   C   D

There, you did it! Write the answers on a postcard, together with your name and address, and send them to Mensa Puzzle Challenge, Mensa House, Freepost, Wolverhampton, WV2 1BR (no stamp needed). If your answers are correct we will send you a certificate and details of how you can apply to become a Mensa member.

Contents

INTRODUCTION

Visual puzzles have always had a special significance for puzzle addicts everywhere. They do not rely on learned skills, as do verbal and numerical conundrums, but test your native wit in the most direct way possible. It is not coincidence that psychologists rely heavily on what they call "non-verbal reasoning" when it comes to assessing intelligence. They have discovered that people who may be at a disadvantage when forced to rely on school learning, can shine forth when allowed the freedom provided by visual puzzles.

The way we tackle such puzzles is also interesting. They lend themselves particularly to sudden flashes of insight so that you find you "know" the answer even before you have worked out logically why it must be so. This is a valuable ability and one that can be encouraged by practice. Of course, as the logic involved in the puzzles gets tougher you will find that you still have to do quite a bit of thinking but, even so, get in the habit of having a hunch about these puzzles first – you'll be surprised how often you will be right.

These puzzles are the work of one of Mensa's highly inventive members, John Bremner. Preparing this book entailed not only stretching his extraordinary powers of creativity to the limits, but also involved hours of painstaking checking on the part of our regular puzzler, David Ballheimer, and of course the invaluable contribution of our illustrators and designers.

Why not join us at Mensa?

Mensa is a unique social club. There is only one criterion for entering Mensa and that is the ability to pass an intelligence test within the top two per cent. We have well over 100,000 members in countries throughout the world. The members meet for social and intellectual stimulation and soon find themselves part of a true "intelligence network" which spans the globe. What is more, with the internet, they find contact with other Mensans throughout the world has never been easier.

You can contact British Mensa at: British Mensa Limited, Mensa House, St John's Square, Wolverhampton, WV2 4AH England (tel 01902 772771).

You can contact Mensa in America at American Mensa Inc., 201 Main Street, Suite 1101, Fort Worth, Texas 76102 USA. American Mensa also have an email address: 70107.2242@compuserve.com and if you would like to join via the internet, the web site is http://www.mwm.org/membform.htm/

If you don't live in the USA or Britain, you can contact Mensa International, 15 The Ivories, 628 Northampton Street, London N1 2NY, England who will be happy to put you in touch with your own national Mensa.

R. P. Allen

Robert Allen
Editorial Director
British Mensa Ltd

Draw three straight lines that will give you six sections with 1 clock, 2 hares and 3 lightning bolts in each section. The lines do not have to go from one edge to another.

see answer 11

This figure is a collection of blocks rotated through four perspectives. How many blocks are there in total?

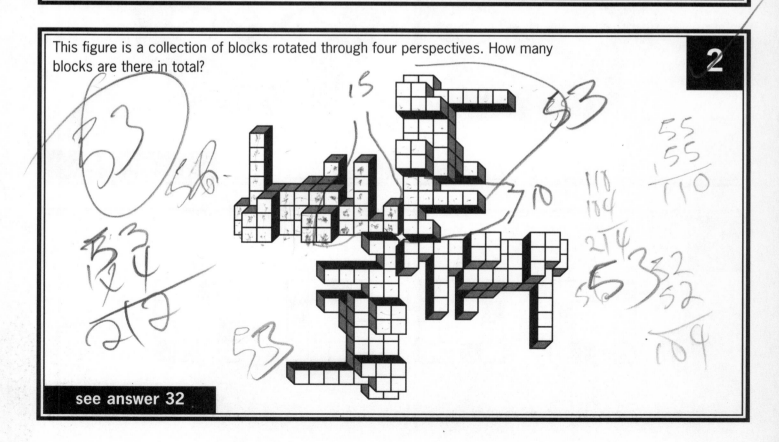

see answer 32

3 Which two of these butterflies are identical?

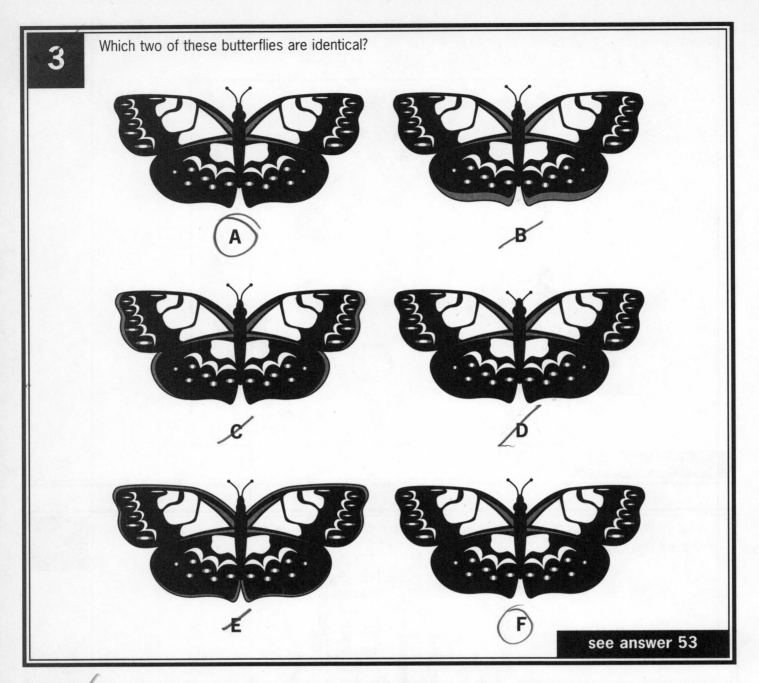

A

B

C

D

E

F

see answer 53

4 Which of the following is the odd one out?

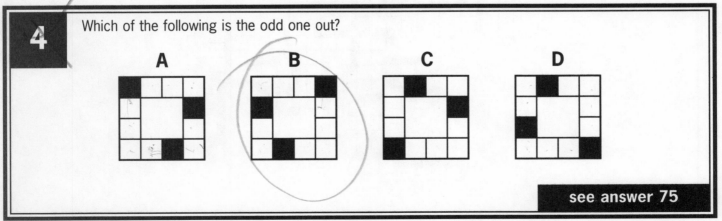

A   B   C   D

see answer 75

Which panel goes in the gap?

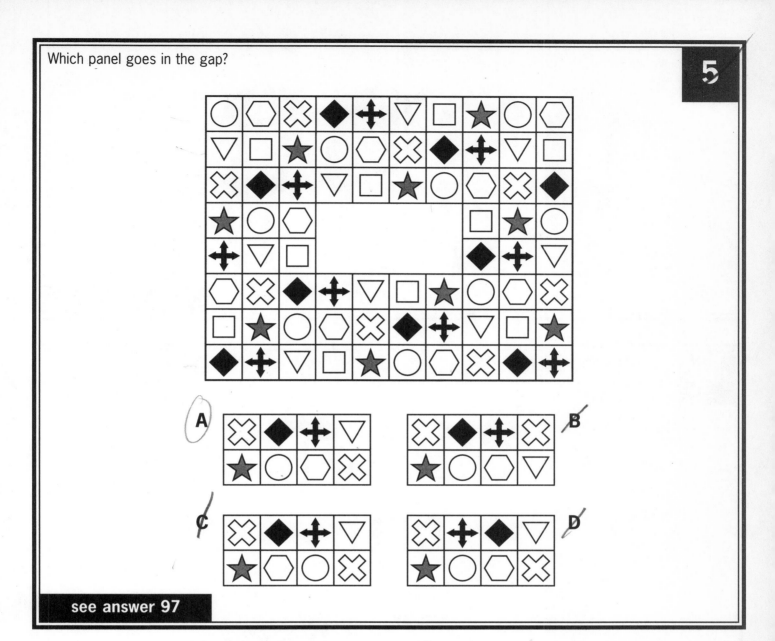

A

B

C

D

see answer 97

Which of the following is the odd one out?

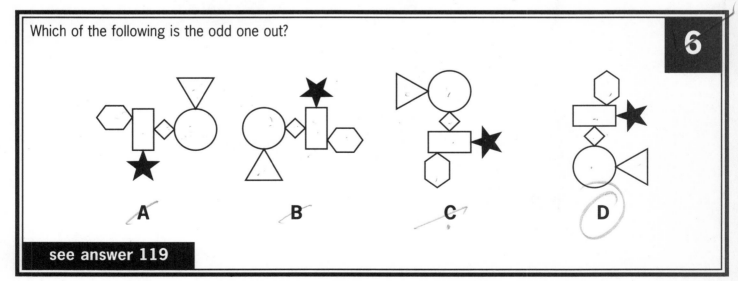

A   B   C   D

see answer 119

7 Which of the following penguins is the odd one out?

A   B   C   D

see answer 141

8 Complete the analogy.

is to

as **DIRT** is to **?**

A

B

C

D

E

F

see answer 162

Which of the following is the odd one out?

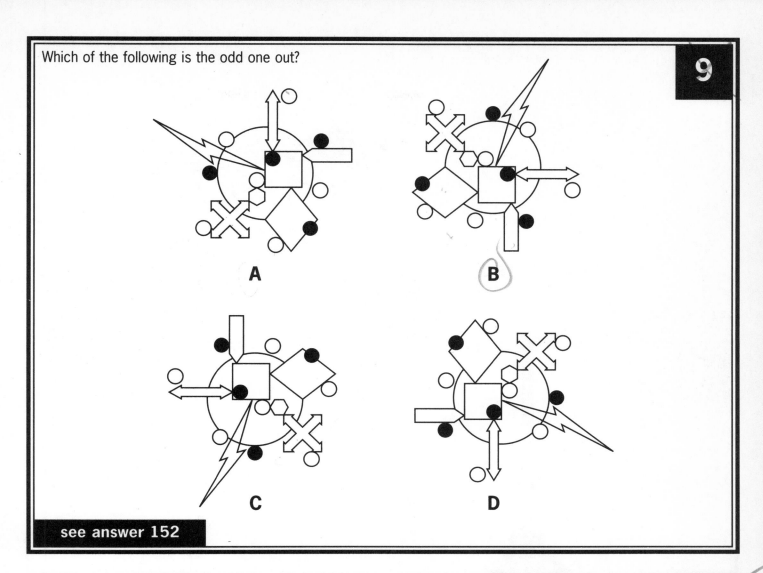

A

B

C

D

see answer 152

How many black spotted tiles are missing from this design?

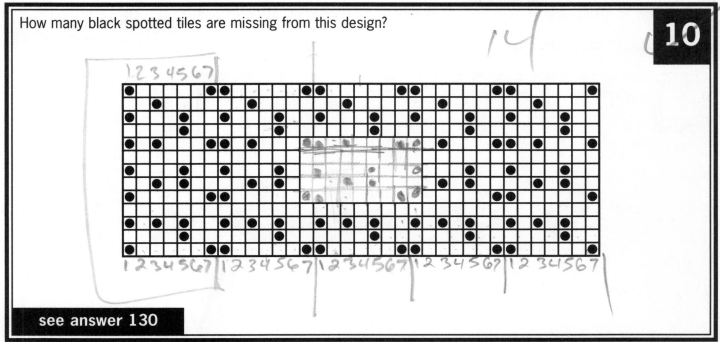

see answer 130

11

If the black arrow pulls in the direction indicated, will the load rise or fall?

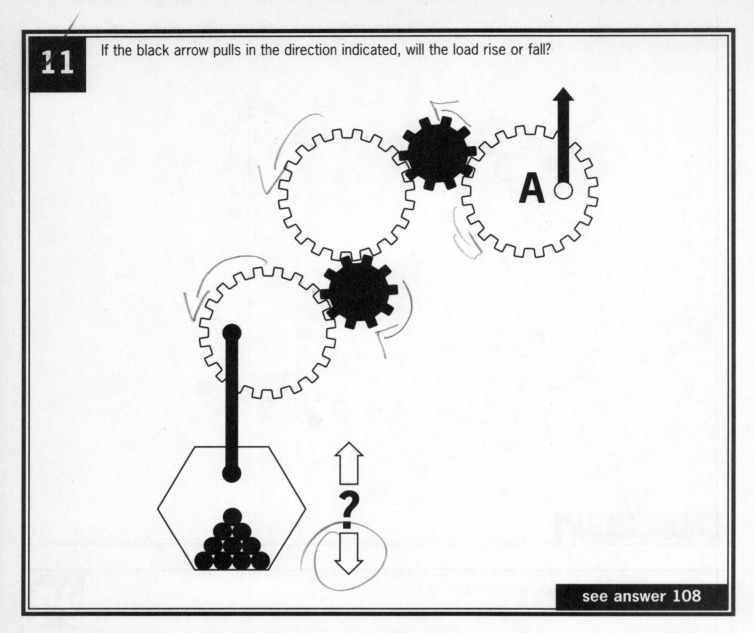

see answer 108

12

Which two birds are identical?

A   B   C   D

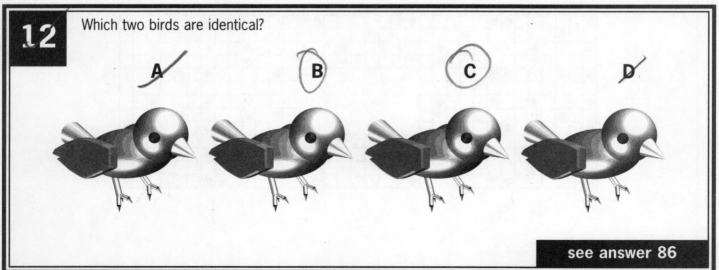

see answer 86

When old gardener Lincoln died, he left his grandchildren 19 rose bushes each. The grandchildren, Agnes (A), Billy (B), Catriona (C) and Derek (D), hated each other, and so decided to fence off their plots as shown. Who had to build the greatest run of fence?

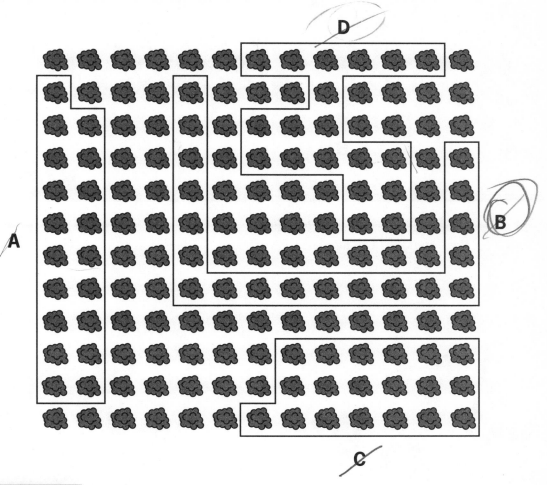

see answer 64

Which of these spiders and their webs make two identical pairs?

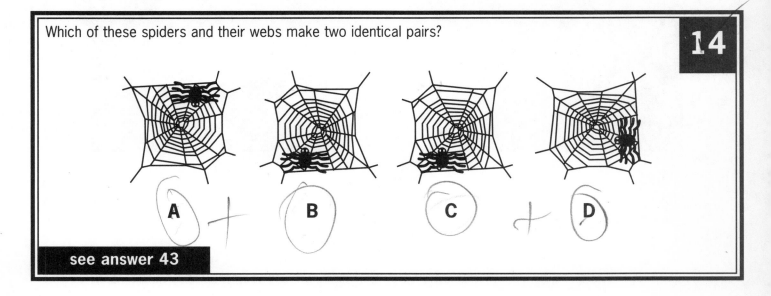

A   B   C   D

see answer 43

15

Which of the following is the odd one out?

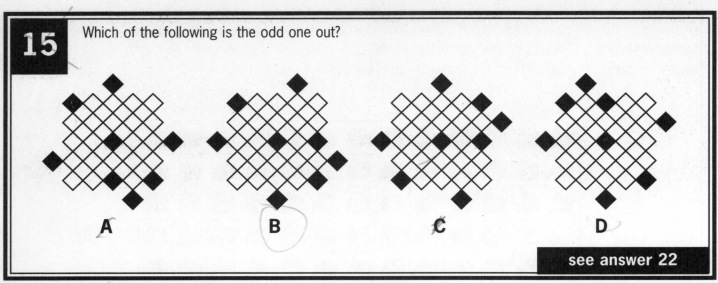

A B C D

see answer 22

16

Spot the 10 differences in picture B.

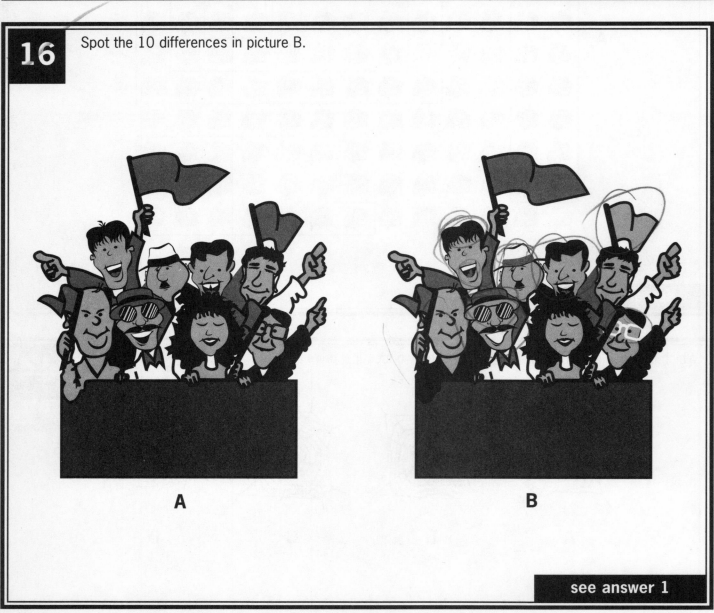

A B

see answer 1

Shade in this map of the USA Midwest using no more than 4 tints, so that no adjacent borders have the same hue.

17

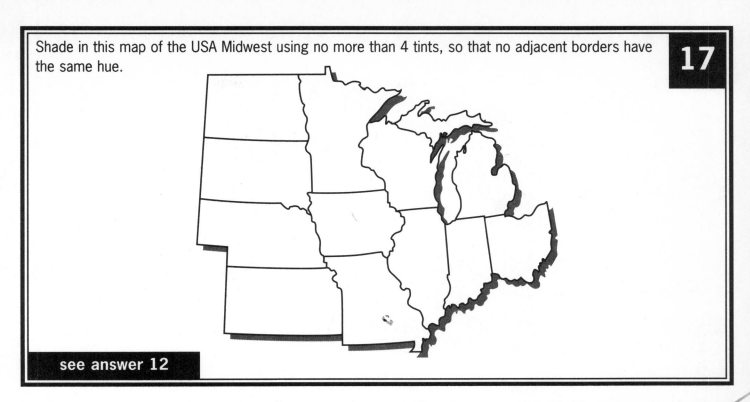

see answer 12

Which of the following is the odd one out?

18

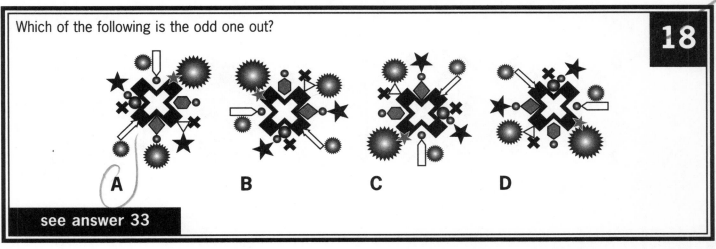

A   B   C   D

see answer 33

Which of the following is the odd one out?

19

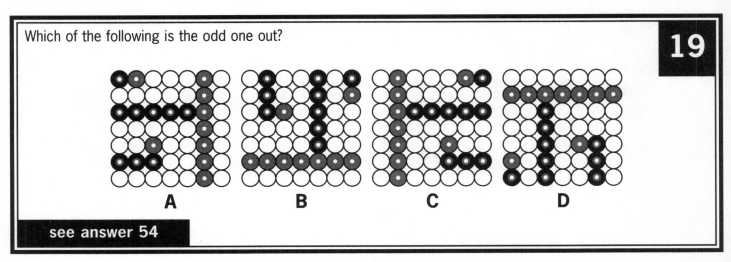

A   B   C   D

see answer 54

---

20 How many bricks are missing from this wall?

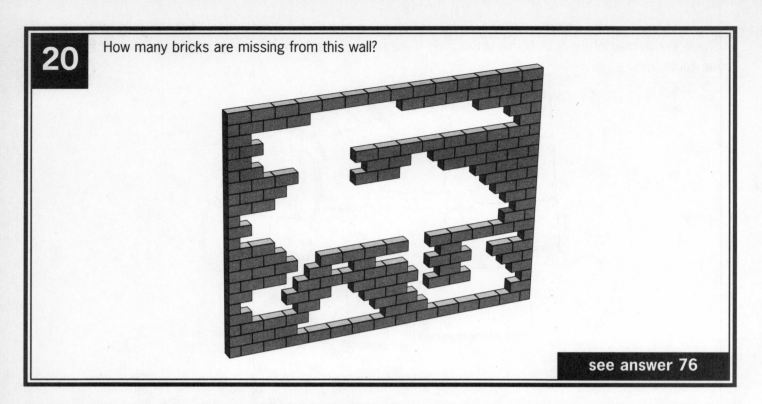

see answer 76

21 Which of the following is the odd one out?

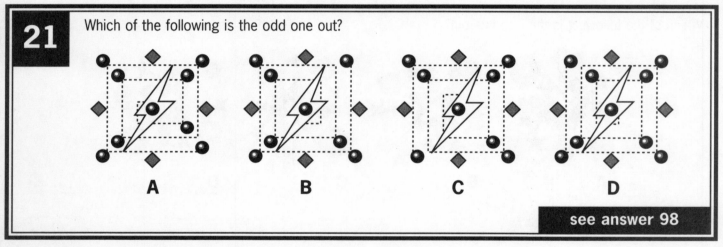

A   B   C   D

see answer 98

22 Which shape should replace the question mark, A, B, C, or D?

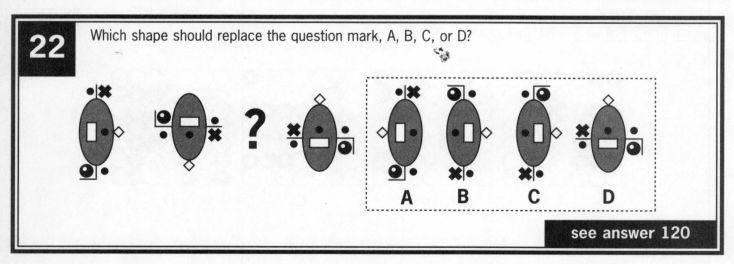

A   B   C   D

see answer 120

16

Complete the analogy.

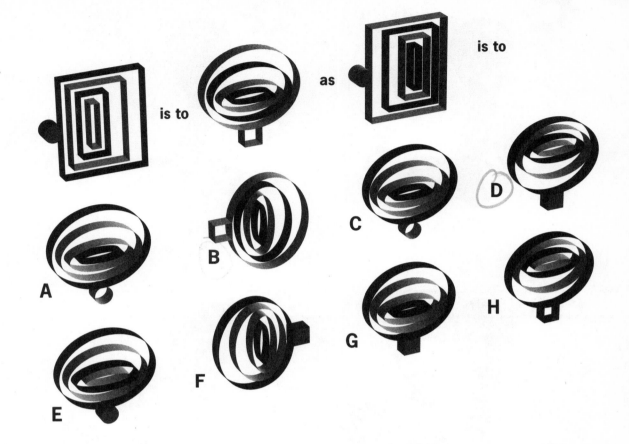

is to

as

is to

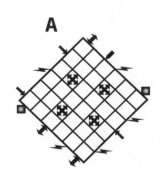

A

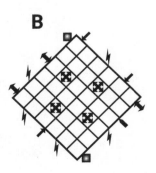

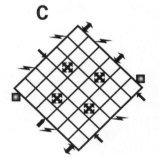

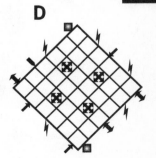

see answer 142

Which of the following is the odd one out?

A   B   C   D

see answer 163

There is something wrong with one of the items in a set. Which one?

A

B

C

D

E

F

see answer 153

Complete the addition.

If 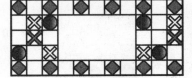 + =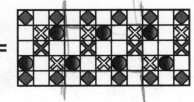

Then 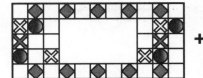 + = **?**

A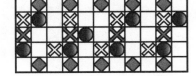

B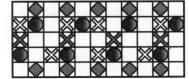

C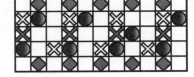

D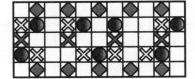

E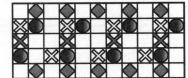

F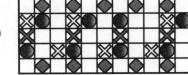

see answer 131

Which tile should replace the question mark? The top and bottom boxes may move independently of each other.

  ?

A B C D

see answer 109

28

Complete the analogy.

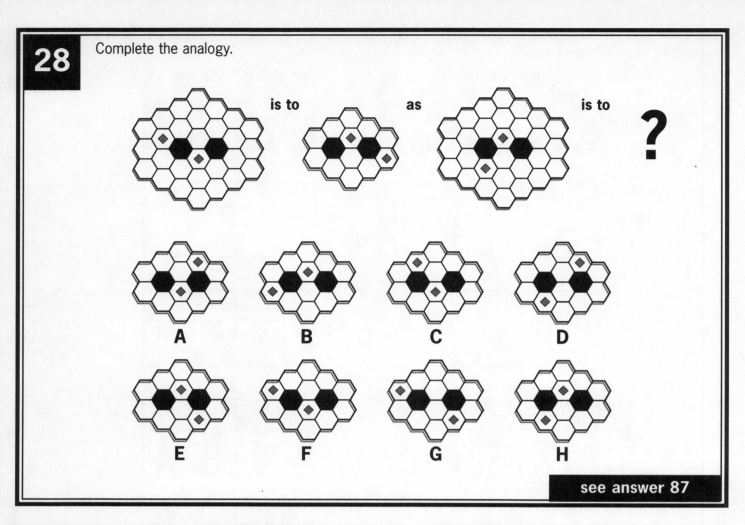

is to ... as ... is to **?**

A B C D

E F G H

see answer 87

29

Find the 8 differences in picture B.

A

B

see answer 65

Find the two shapes that don't go with the other three.

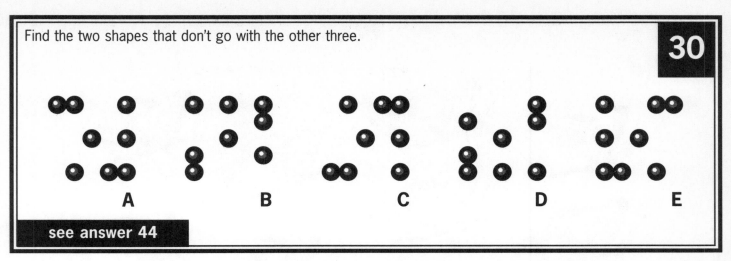

A   B   C   D   E

see answer 44

This system is in balance. The black block weighs the same as the pale blocks. If three more blocks are placed on the black block, where should two pale blocks be placed to return the system to balance?

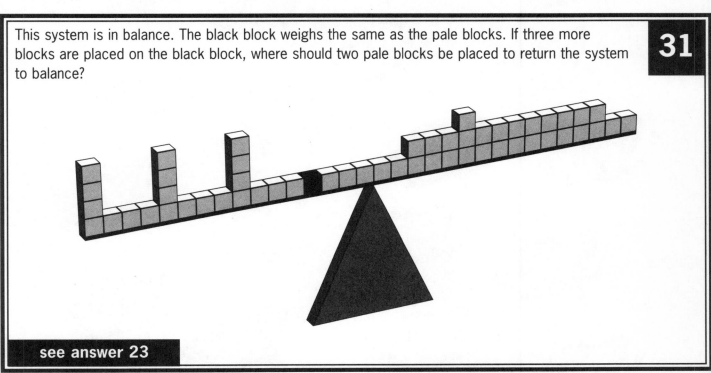

see answer 23

Which of the following is the odd one out?

A   B   C   D

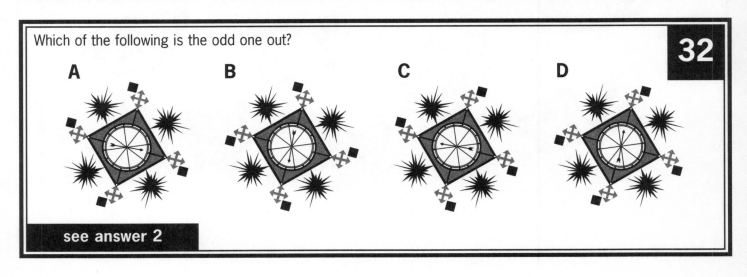

see answer 2

Only two of these butterflies are identical. Which are they?

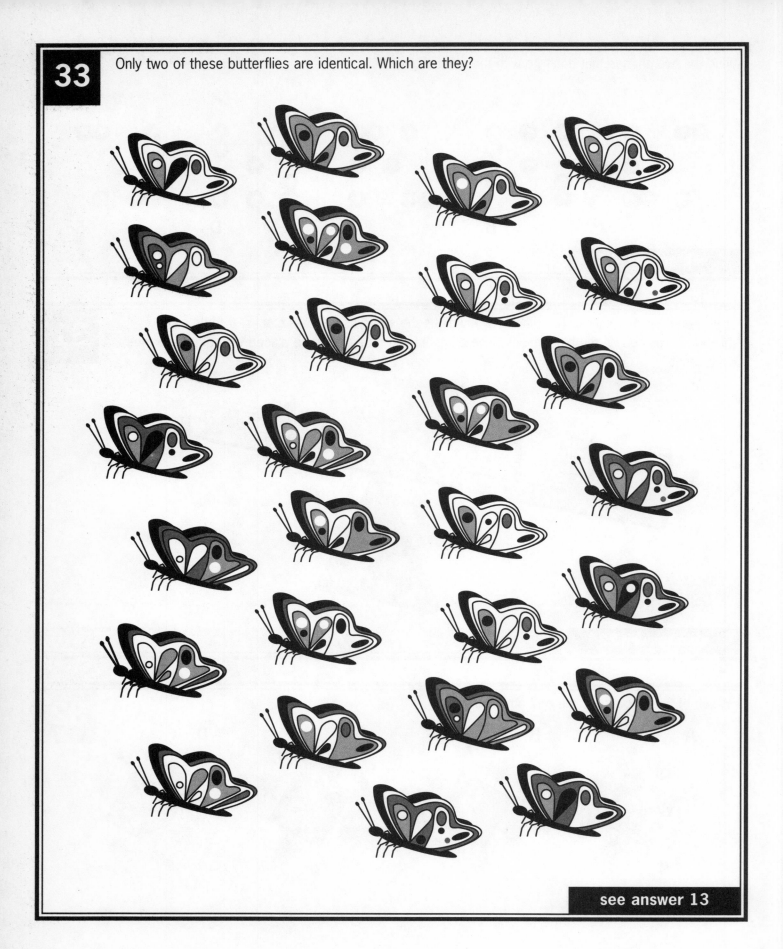

see answer 13

Which is the missing panel?

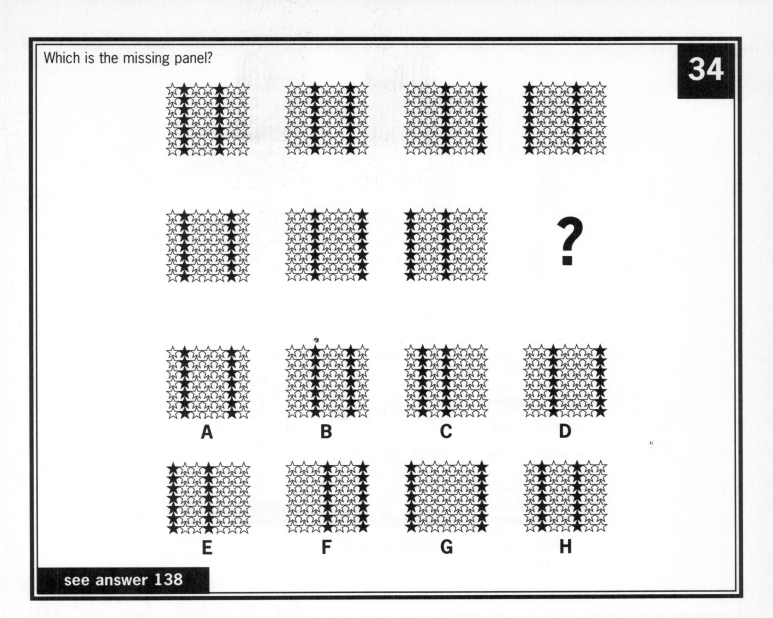

A   B   C   D

E   F   G   H

see answer 138

How many kangaroos are in this herd?

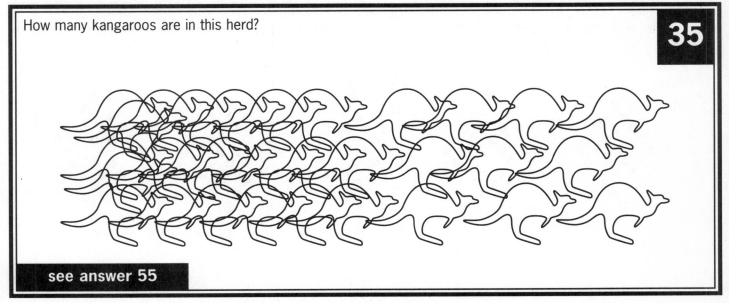

see answer 55

Complete the analogy.

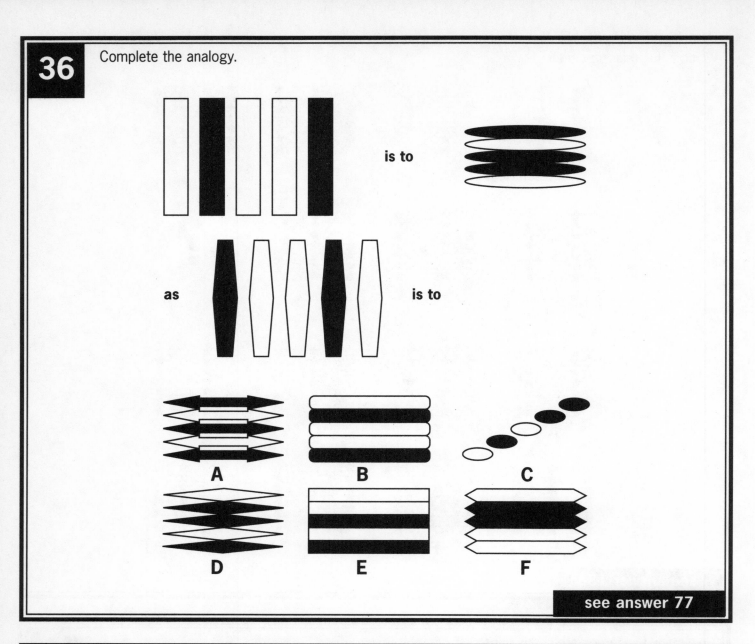

is to

as

is to

A

B

C

D

E

F

see answer 77

Which two patterns do not go with the other three?

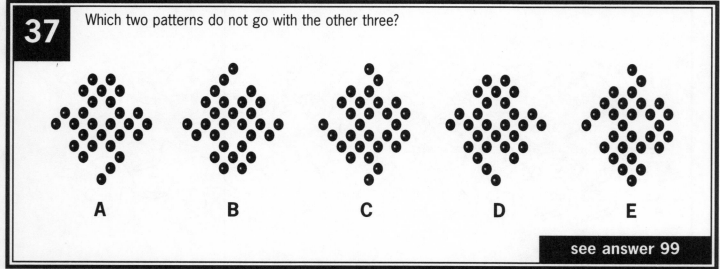

A   B   C   D   E

see answer 99

A

B

C

D

see answer 121

39

What comes next in this series?

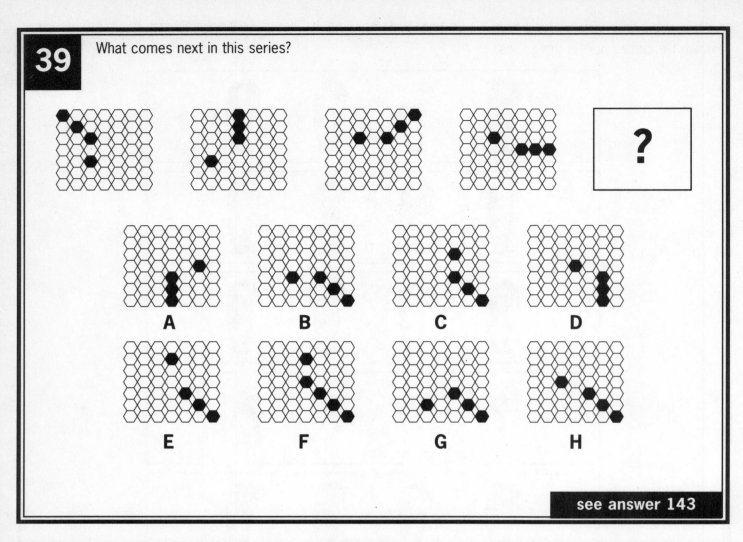

see answer 143

40

If the wheel at A is turned as indicated, will the load first rise, or fall?

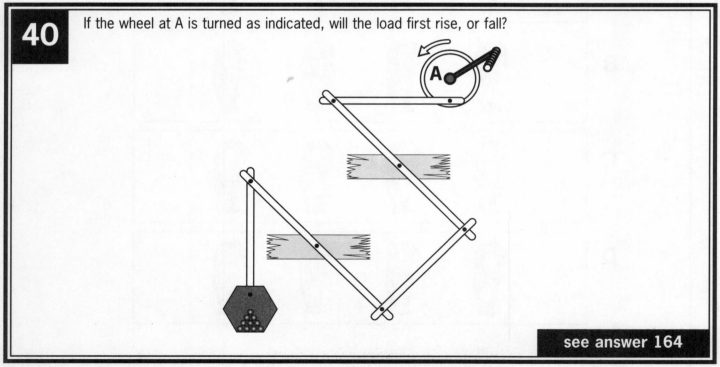

see answer 164

If a brick is dropped from the top of a cliff (on a planet with no atmosphere) at the same time that a projectile is fired parallel with the ground from a large gun, will:

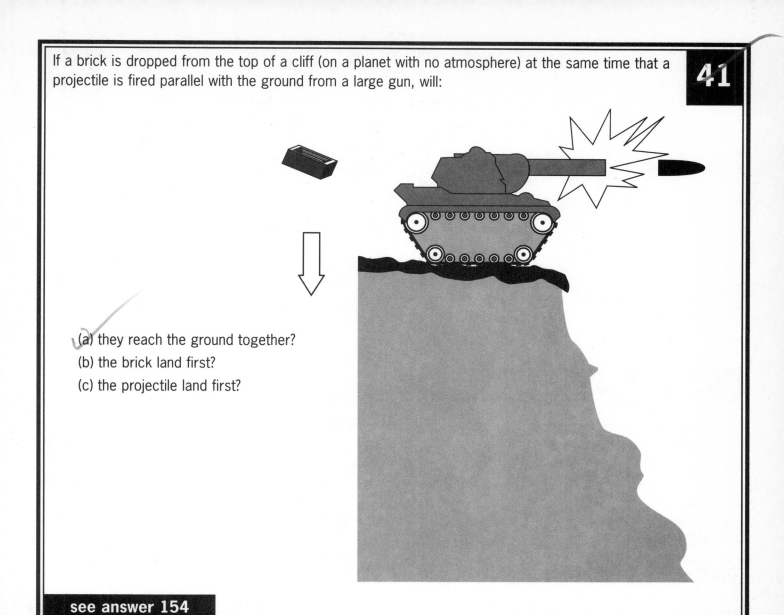

(a) they reach the ground together?

(b) the brick land first?

(c) the projectile land first?

see answer 154

Which of the following is the odd one out?

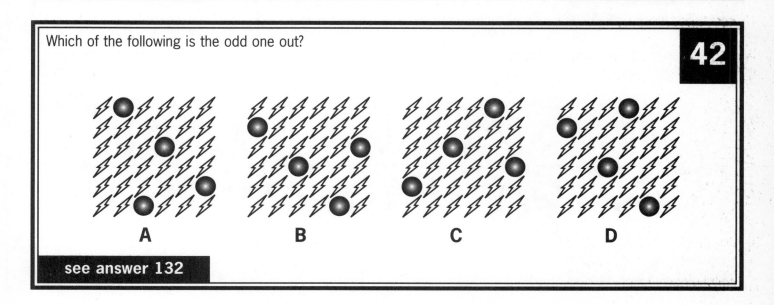

A   B   C   D

see answer 132

The black dots represent hinge points. If points A and B are moved together, will points C and D move together or apart?

43

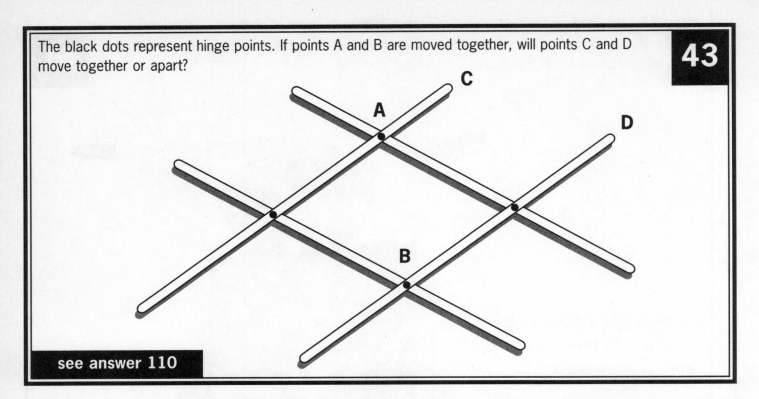

see answer 110

Which of the following is the odd one out?

44

A   B   C   D

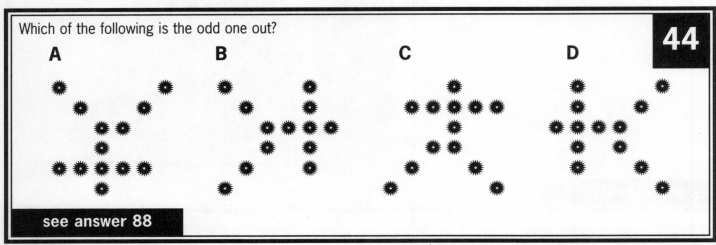

see answer 88

Which of the following is the odd one out?

45

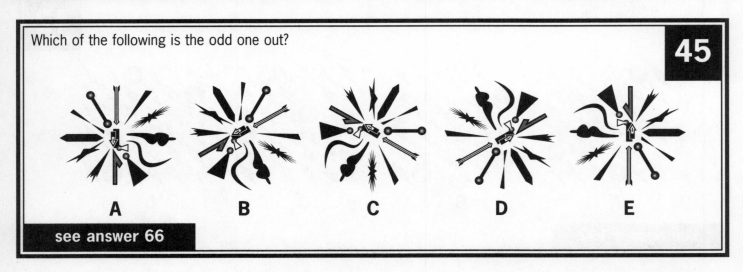

A   B   C   D   E

see answer 66

Draw four straight lines that divide this puzzle into seven sections, with 3 pyramids and 7 balls in each section. The lines do not have to go from one edge to another.

46

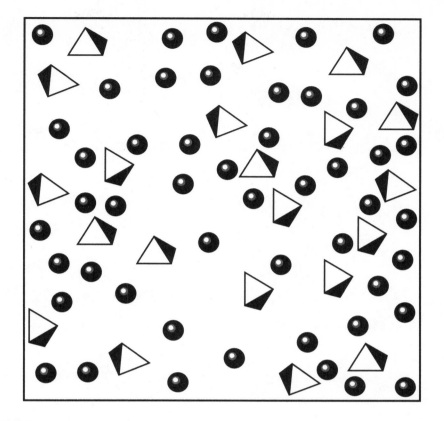

see answer 150

Which set of shapes fits into the middle of this panel to complete the pattern?

47

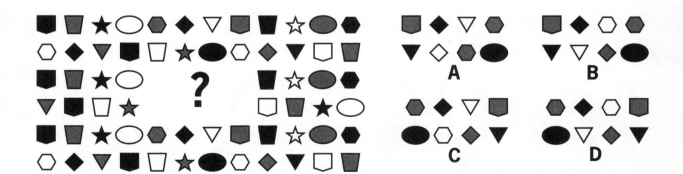

see answer 24

48 Which of the following make three pairs of identical scenes?

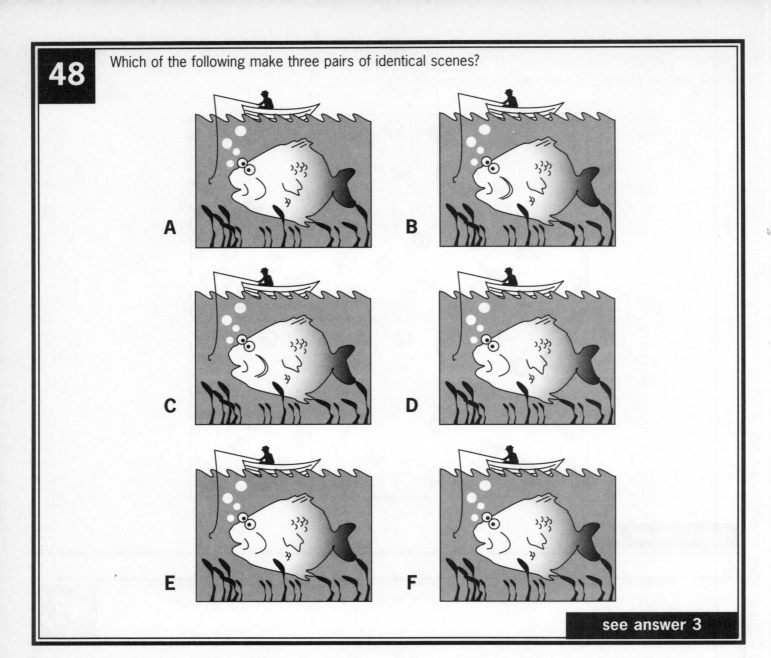

see answer 3

49 Which of the following is the odd one out?

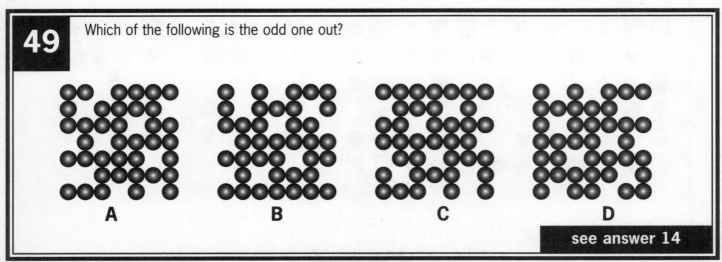

see answer 14

Find the 8 places where the routes meet to form crossroads rather than crossovers.

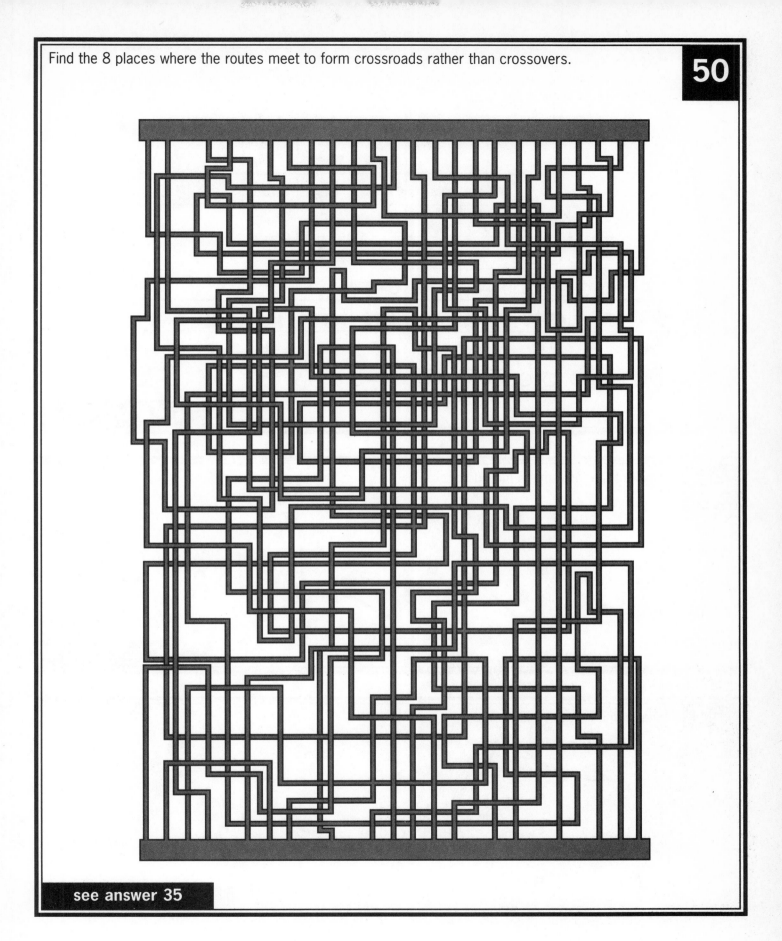

see answer 35

51

Here is a long multiplication sum. Each symbol represents a number from 0 to 9, and each like symbol always represents the same number. With this in mind, which symbol should replace the question mark?

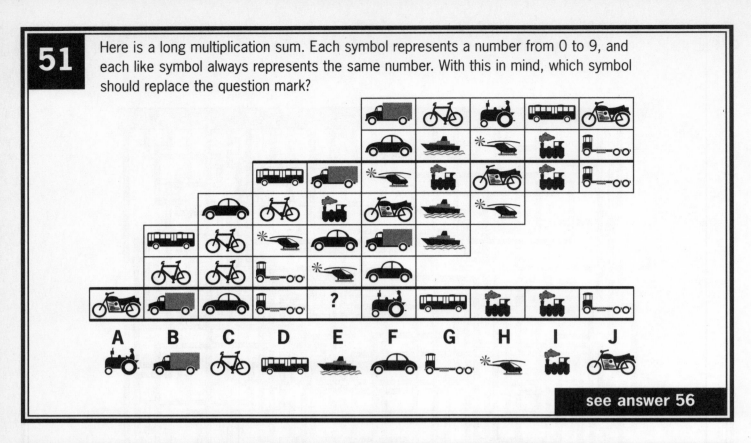

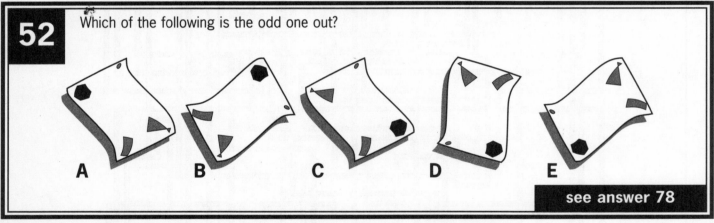

see answer 56

52

Which of the following is the odd one out?

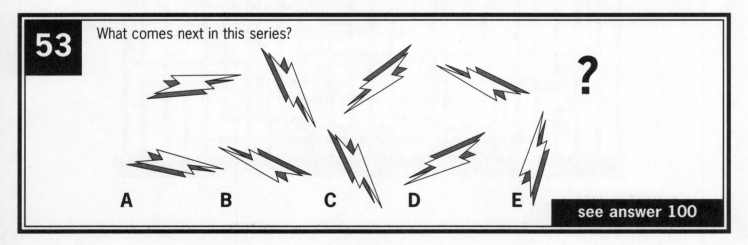

A   B   C   D   E

see answer 78

53

What comes next in this series?

?

A   B   C   D   E

see answer 100

Complete the analogy.

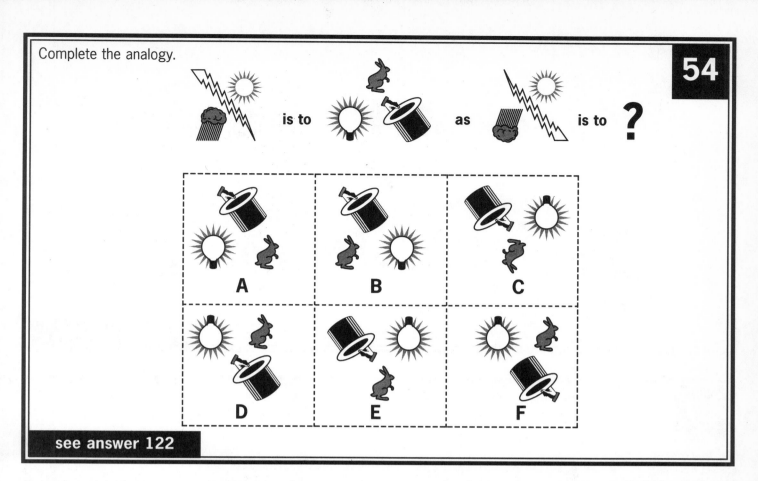

see answer 122

What would this pyramid look like opened out?

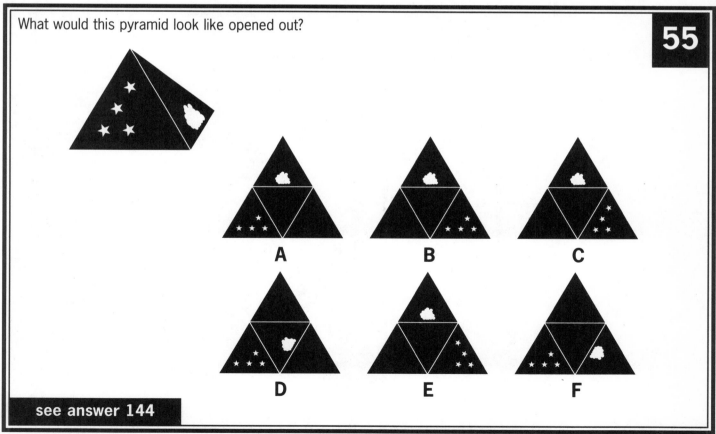

see answer 144

56

Which two of these form an identical pair that do not go with the other eight?

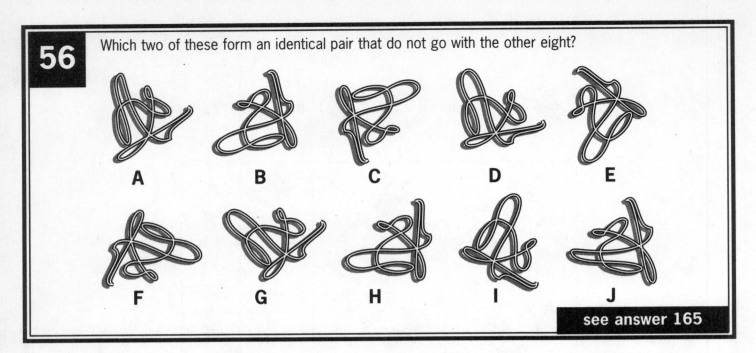

A   B   C   D   E

F   G   H   I   J

see answer 165

57

In this system of levers and rollers the black spots are fixed swivel points and the shaded spots are non-fixed swivel points. With this in mind, if the lever is pushed as shown, will the load rise or fall?

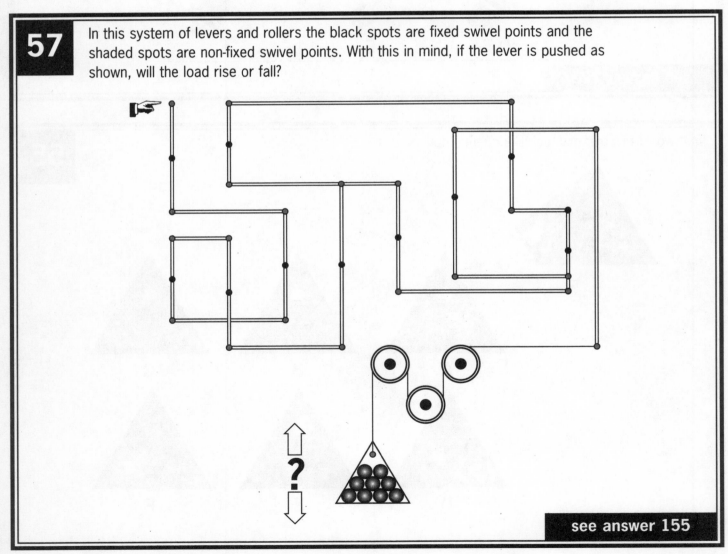

see answer 155

Which of the following is the odd one out?

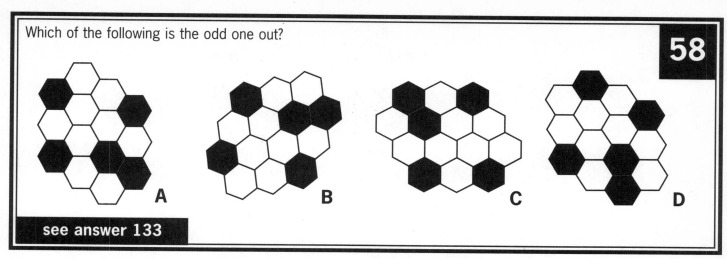

A   B   C   D

see answer 133

From the information given, work out the missing total and the values of the different images.

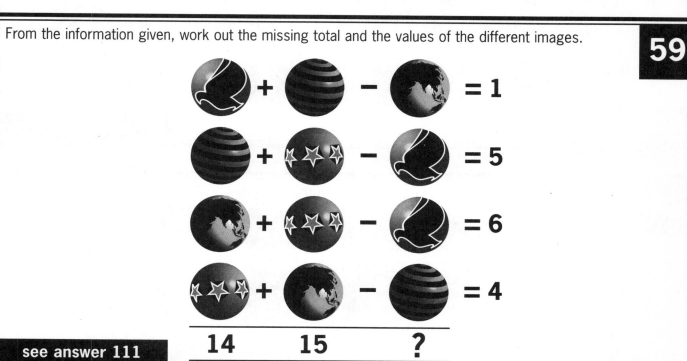

see answer 111

Which of the following is the odd one out?

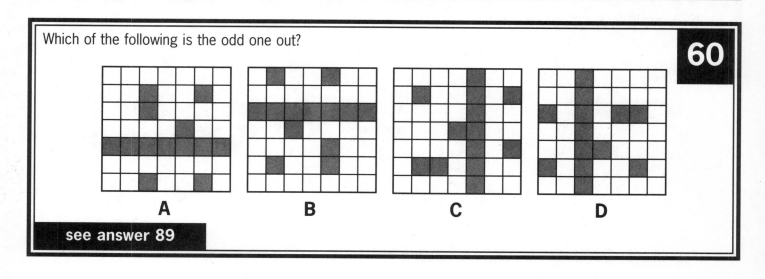

A   B   C   D

see answer 89

61

What comes next in this series?

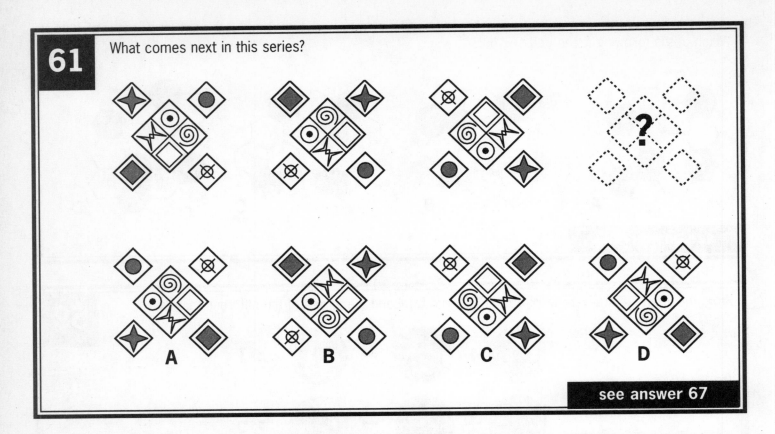

A   B   C   D

see answer 67

62

Which figure or figures below is or are identical to the one in the box?

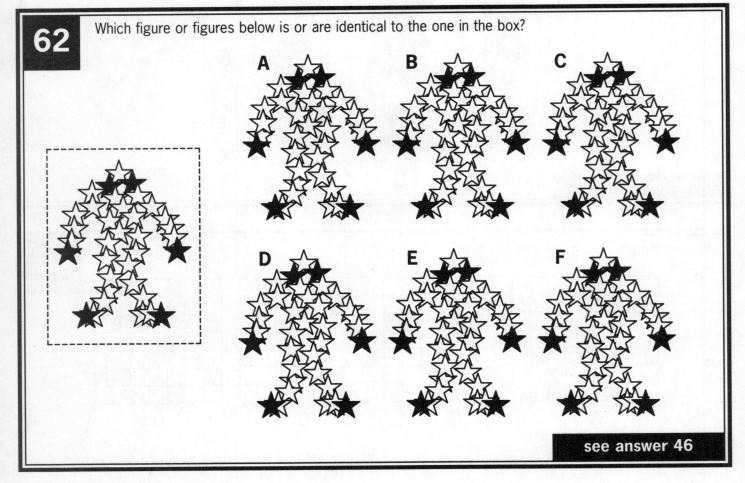

A   B   C

D   E   F

see answer 46

Complete the analogy.

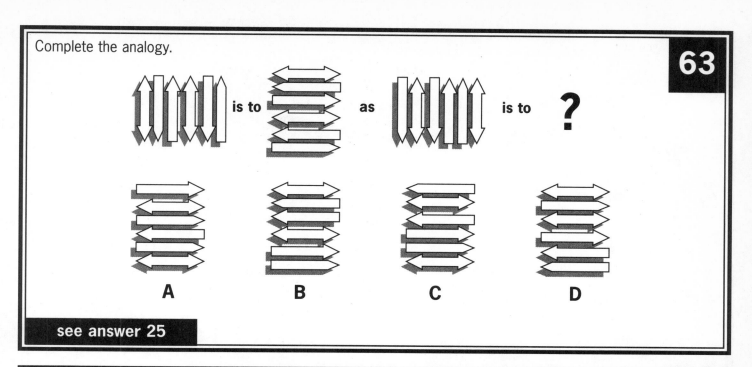

is to ... as ... is to **?**

A   B   C   D

see answer 25

Which pattern below can be used to make the box in the middle?

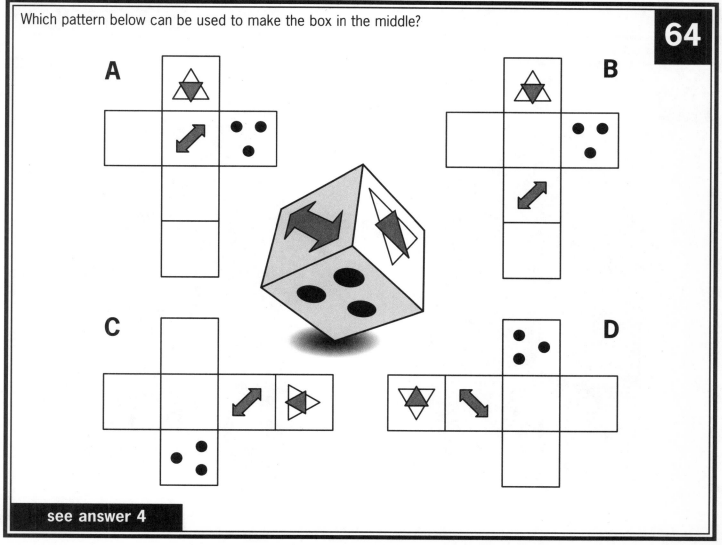

A   B   C   D

see answer 4

65

Which of the following is the odd one out?

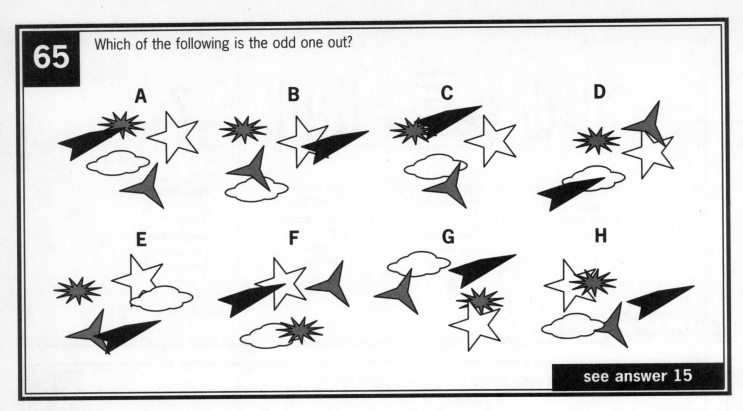

see answer 15

66

Mark the 12 differences in picture B.

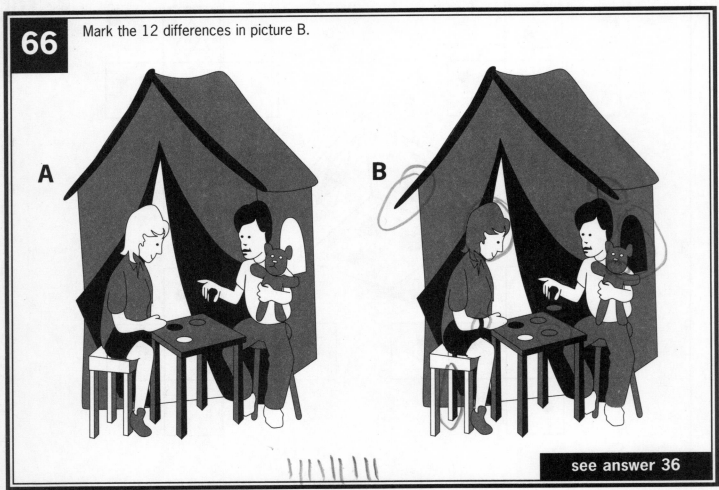

see answer 36

What comes next in this series?

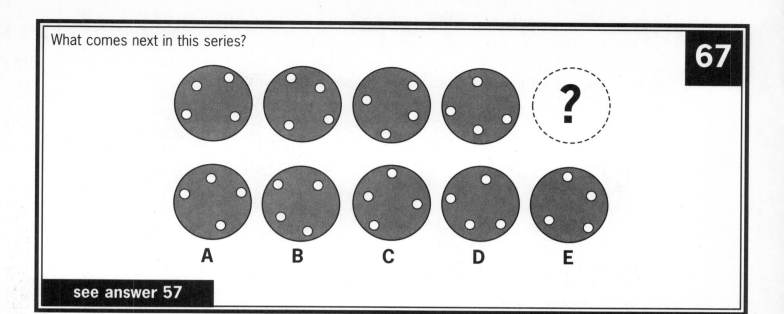

A   B   C   D   E

see answer 57

Draw three straight lines that divide this puzzle into four sections with, respectively, 4, 5, 6 and 7 snakes, drums and clouds in each section. The lines do not have to go from one edge to another.

see answer 101

69

Each like animal has the same value and the bear, horse, fish and bird all have different values. Which of A, B, C, D, E or F is the total value of the single column above the question mark, and what are the lowest possible values of the animals?

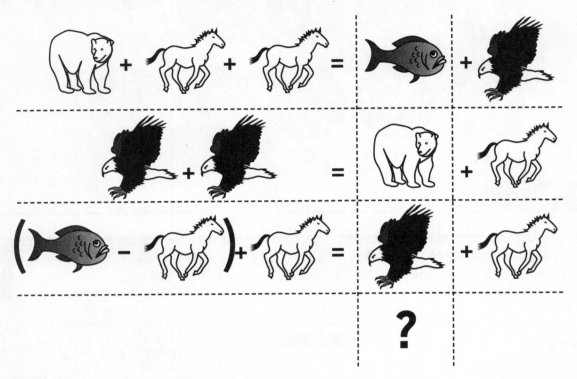

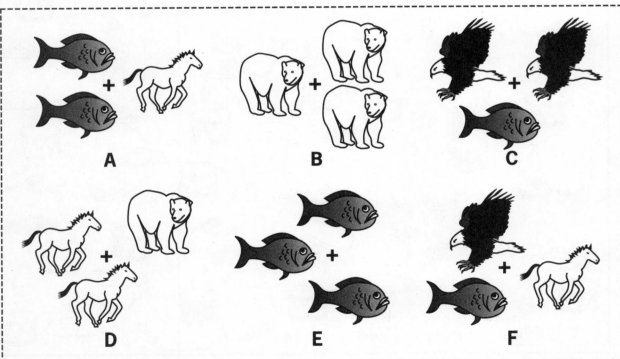

see answer 123

As park ranger on this safari you have to collect as many rattlesnakes as possible without the risk of getting killed or maimed by them or other creatures. The wildcats will eat a part of your body if you step onto a sector which they have scent marked and the bears will hug you to death. The bears and wildcats have marked one segment next to the one they stand on, but you have no way of knowing which one. You may not go back over your tracks. Start on the shaded sector and finish on the snake facing the other way.

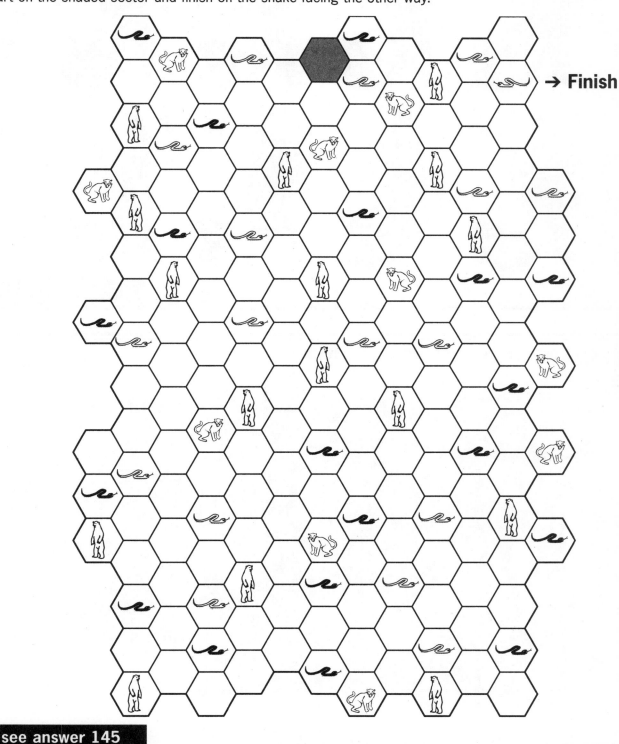

→ **Finish**

see answer 145

71

Which of the following is the odd one out?

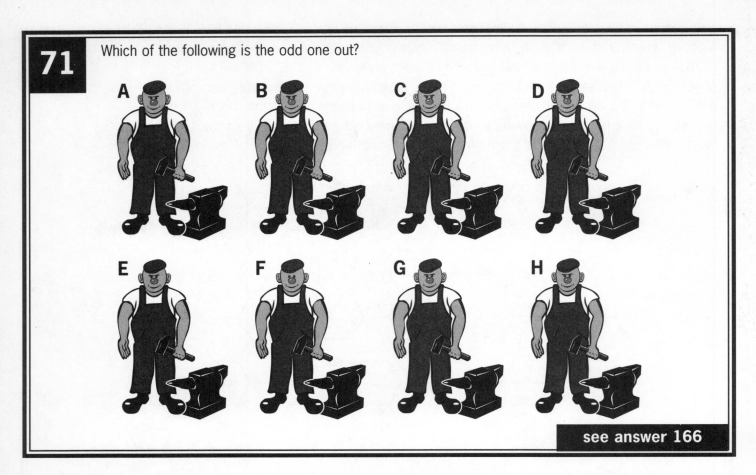

A B C D

E F G H

see answer 166

72

Which one of these strings leads you to the diamond?

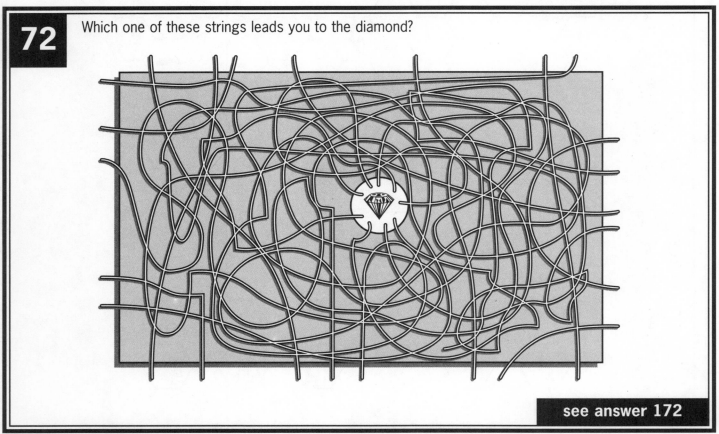

see answer 172

Which of the following is the odd one out?

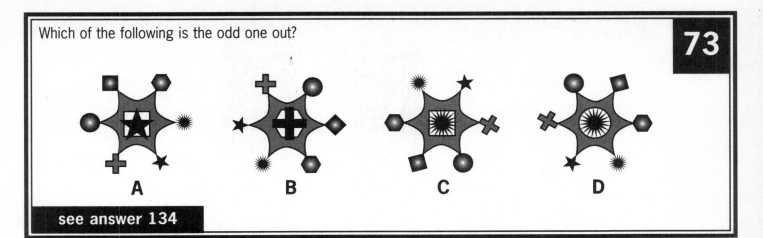

A   B   C   D

see answer 134

Which tile is missing from the following panel?

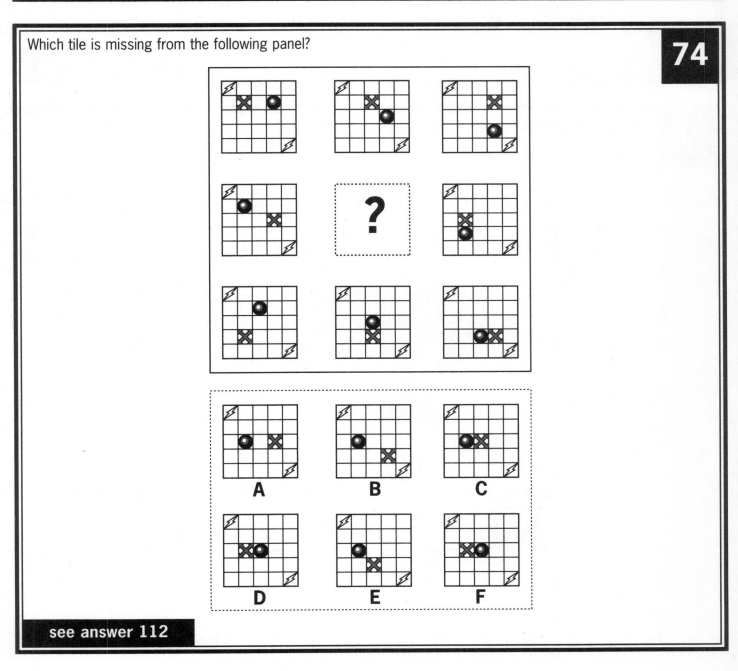

see answer 112

75

What comes next in this series?

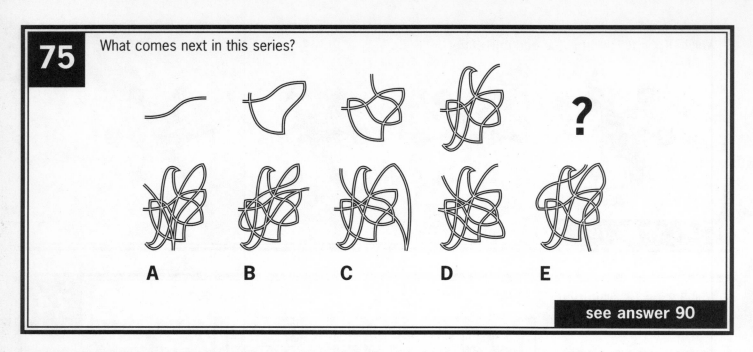

A   B   C   D   E

see answer 90

76

Which of the unfolded shapes is the box in the middle opened out?

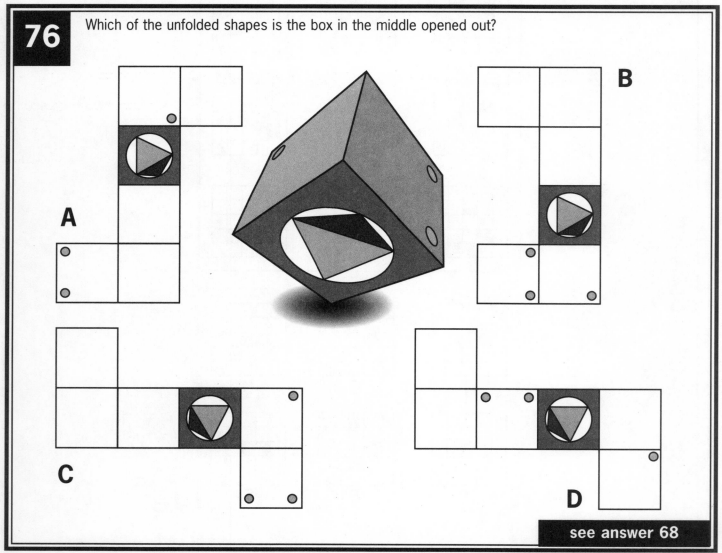

A

B

C

D

see answer 68

Which set does not go with the other three?

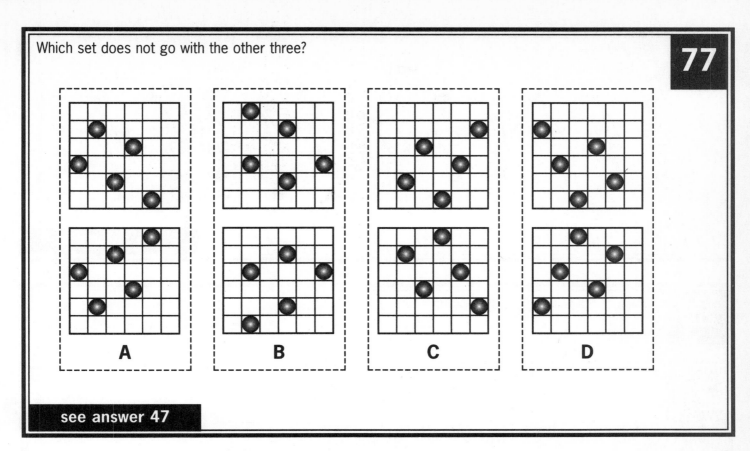

see answer 47

What comes next in this series?

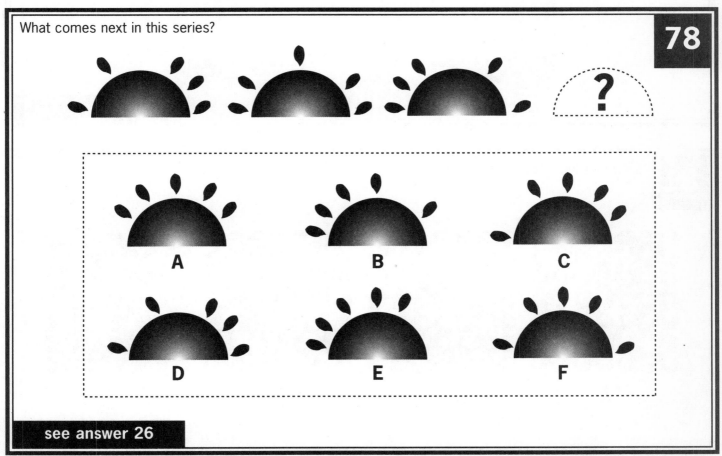

see answer 26

79

What comes next in this series?

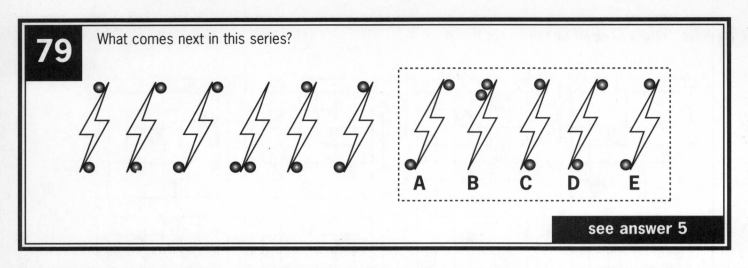

see answer 5

80

Which of the following is the odd one out?

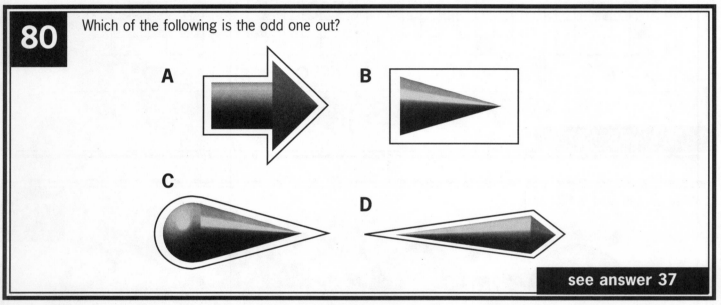

see answer 37

81

Which of the following is the odd one out?

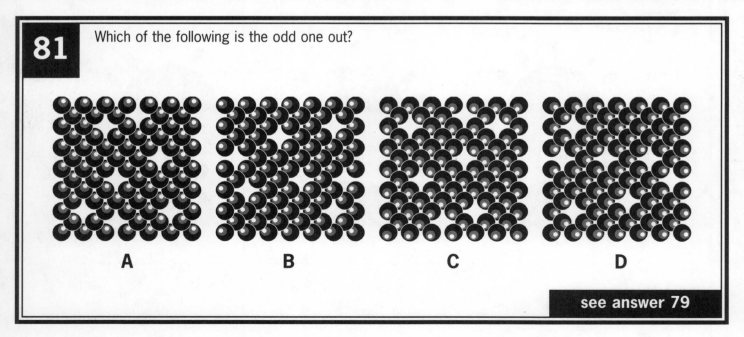

A   B   C   D

see answer 79

Which set should the replace the question mark to complete the pattern?

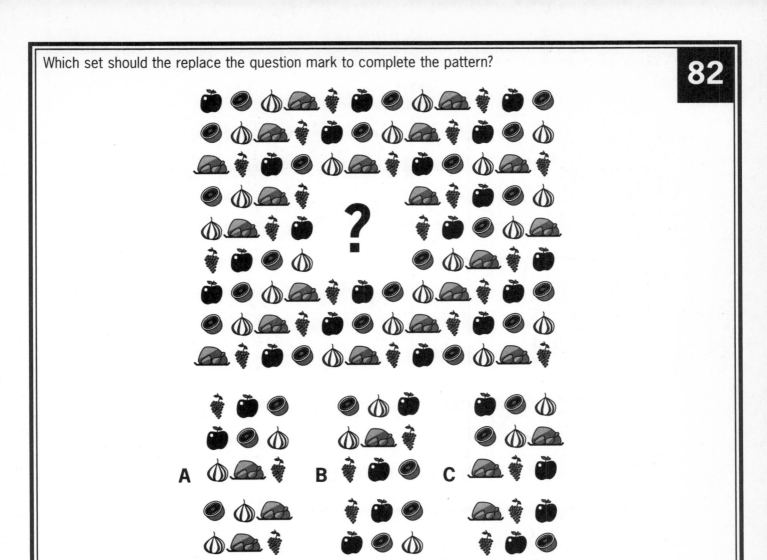

see answer 16

Which of the following is the odd one out?

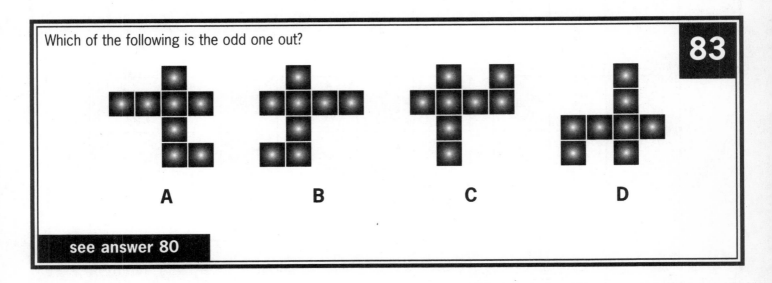

A   B   C   D

see answer 80

84

Which set of tiles goes into the middle to complete the pattern?

A

B

C

D

E

F

see answer 58

Which panel should replace the question mark?

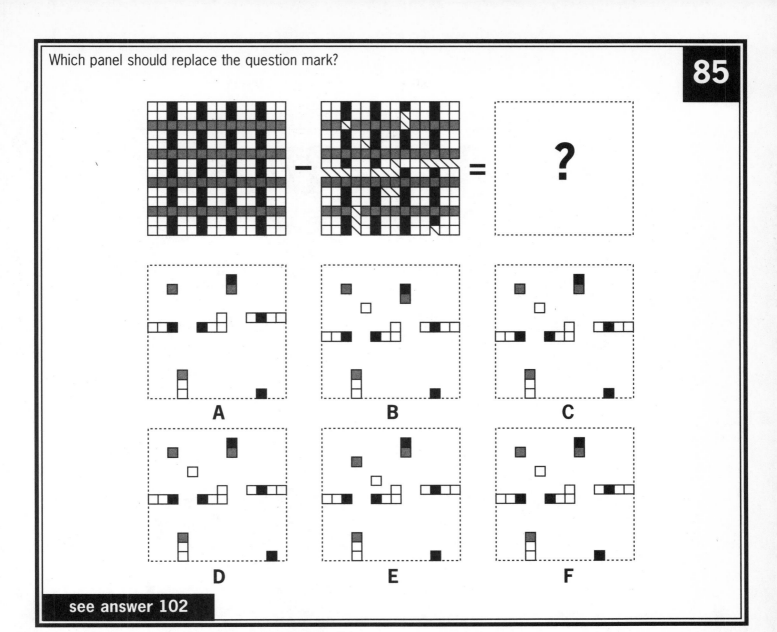

see answer 102

Which of the following is the odd one out?

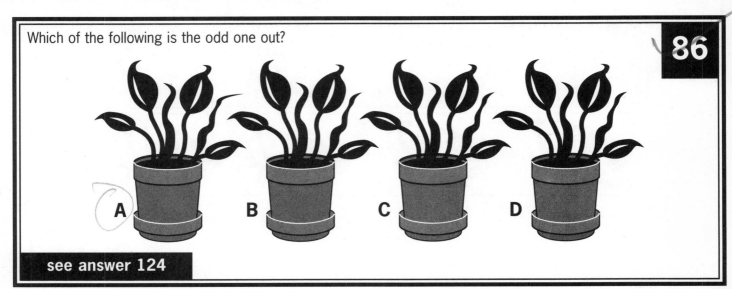

see answer 124

Which tile comes next in this series?

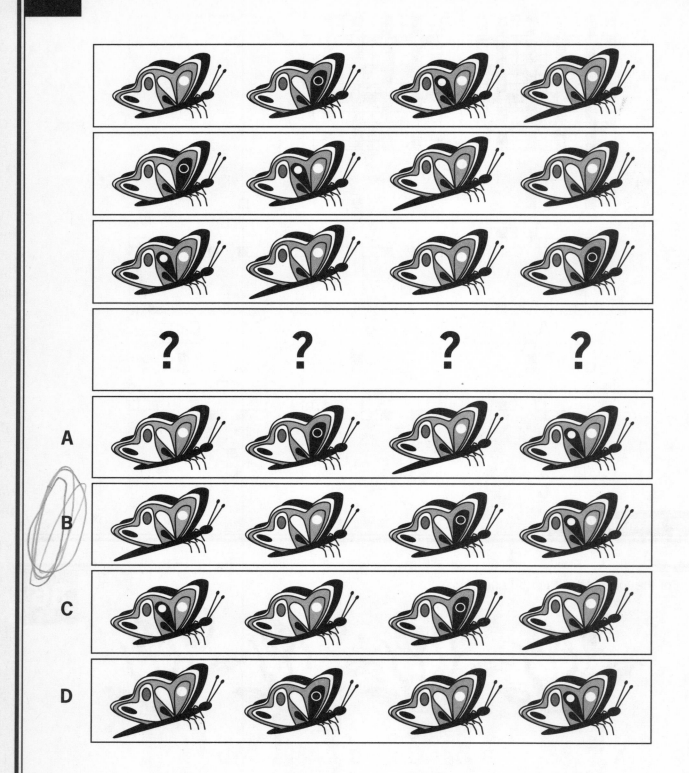

see answer 146

In this system of levers and rollers, in which the shaded spots are non-fixed swivel points and the black spots are fixed swivel points, if the lever is pushed as shown, will each load at A and B rise or fall?

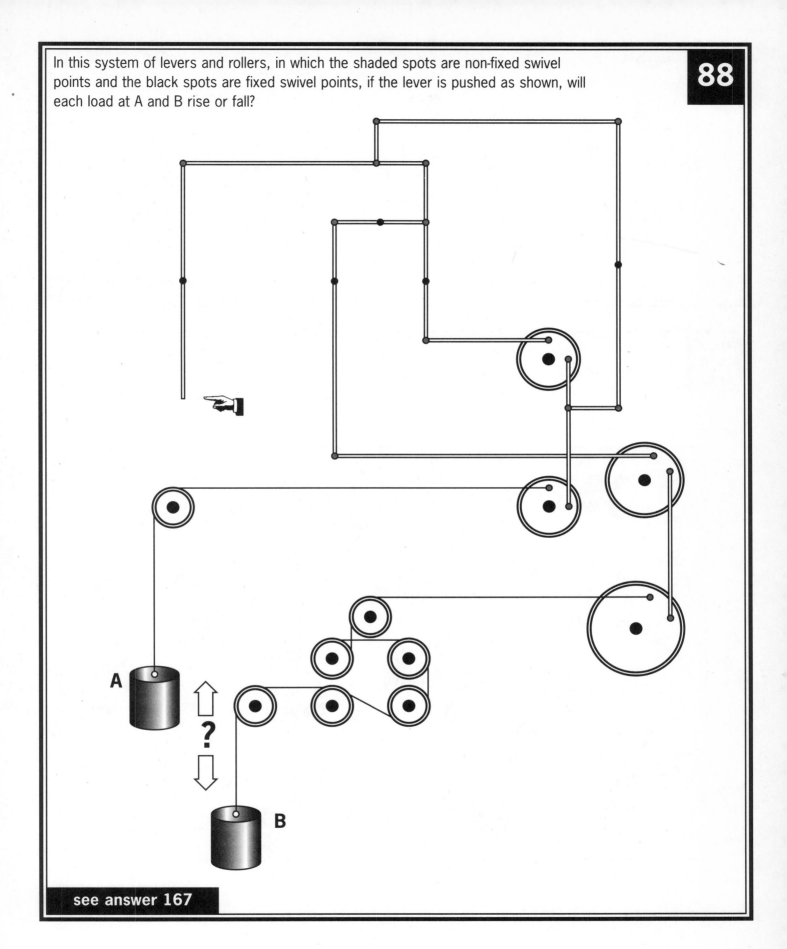

see answer 167

89

Which of the following is the odd one out?

A   B   C   D   E

see answer 156

90

Draw three straight lines that divide this puzzle into six sections that contain 1 fish and 1 flag in each and respectively 0, 1, 2, 3, 4 and 5 drums and lightning bolts. The lines do not have to go from one edge to another.

see answer 135

The symbols in the following calculations represent the numbers from 0 to 9. Each like symbol always represents the same number. What symbol should replace the question mark?

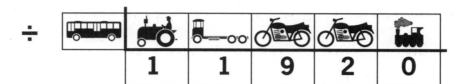

8 9 4 1 6

1 1 9 2 0

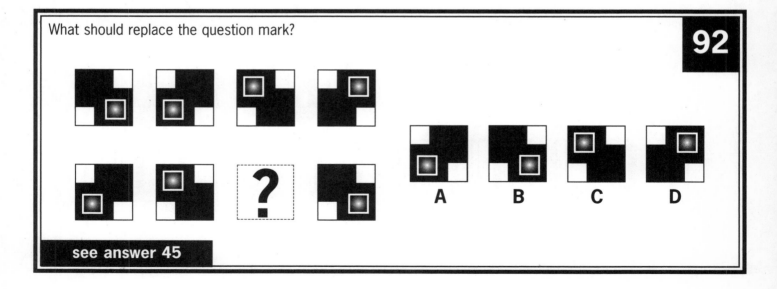

A B C D E

F G H I J

see answer 113

What should replace the question mark?

A B C D

see answer 45

93

In this system of fixed belts and freely revolving pulley wheels, what will happen to the loads A and B when the handle is turned in the direction indicated?

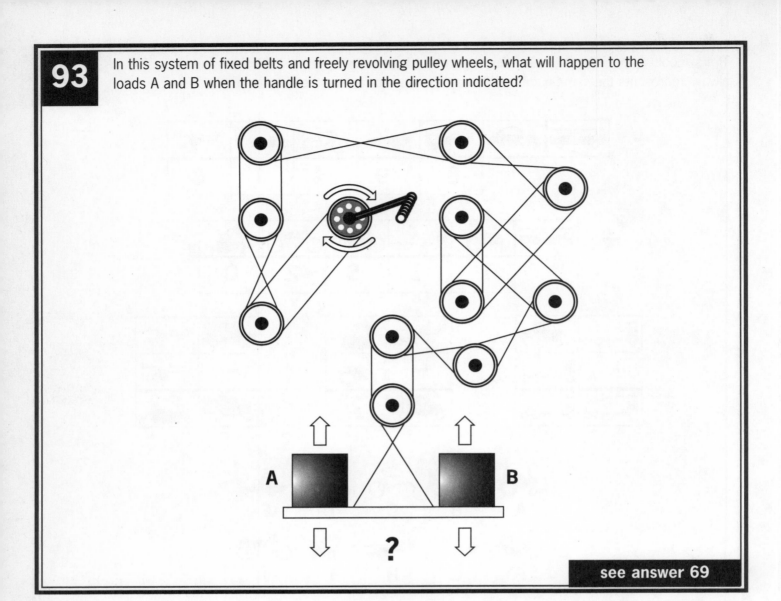

see answer 69

94

What comes next?

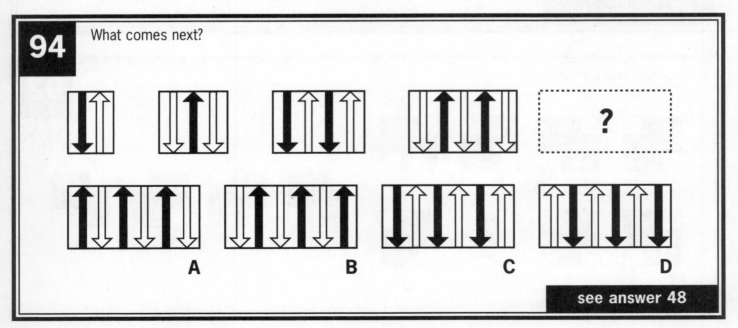

A   B   C   D

see answer 48

What comes next in this series?

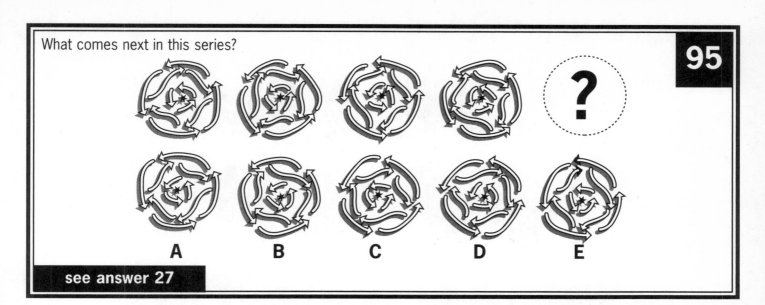

A   B   C   D   E

see answer 27

Complete the analogy.

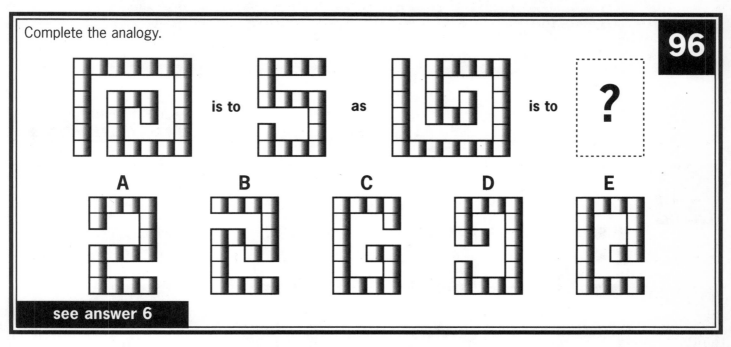

is to ... as ... is to ?

A   B   C   D   E

see answer 6

Which of the following is the odd one out?

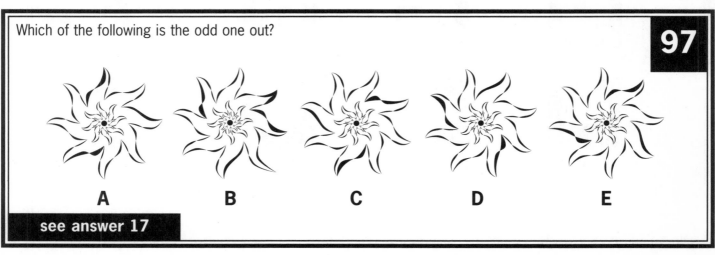

A   B   C   D   E

see answer 17

98

Find the 14 differences in picture B.

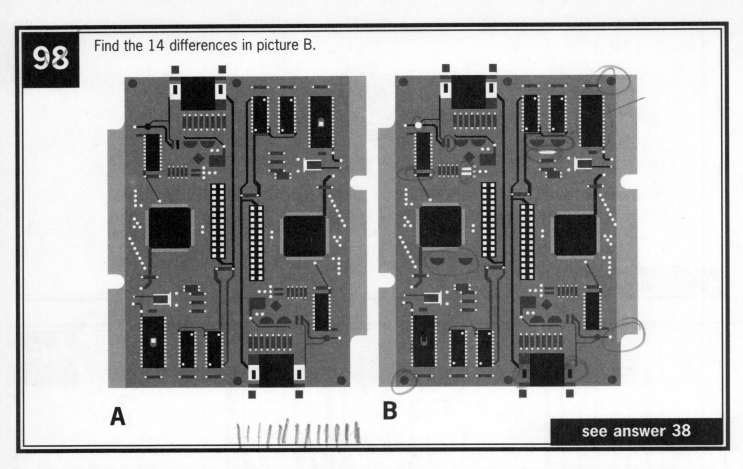

A   B

see answer 38

99

What should replace the question mark?

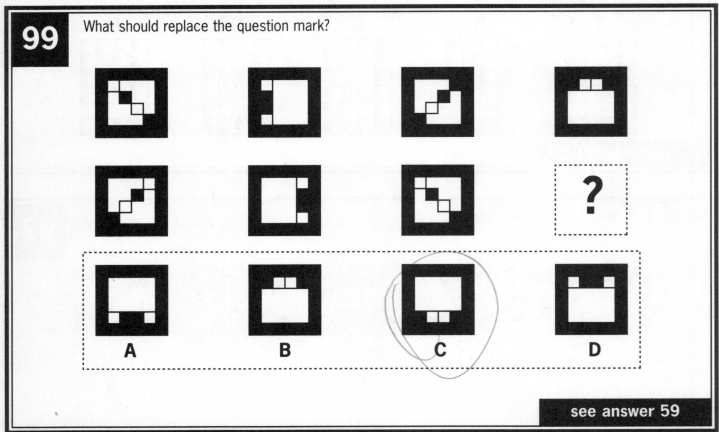

A   B   C   D

see answer 59

The Double Cheeseburger Threat!

Listen carefully! Because of your skill at solving puzzles you are hereby deputized. The President of the United States has been lured to the middle of a web-shaped dungeon, on the promise of a double cheeseburger on rye. Alas, it was a cruel trick and all the doors have slammed shut and trapped the President with a single French fry and no mayonnaise. He is ravenously hungry, and he will go insane if he doesn't get a double cheeseburger within 120 minutes. Even now a plan is beginning to hatch in his hunger-crazed mind to seize control of the world's entire supply of minced beef, cheese and bread rolls, and make a double cheeseburger big enough to flatten Washington. The threat is real, seriously fattening, and full of cholesterol.

Each door (numbered) is guarded by a lock that can only be released by solving a fiendishly difficult puzzle. Can you can complete this task, and get the double cheese-burger to the President before he goes insane? Or should we go with the alternative plan and ask all the Elvis wannabes of the world to head for Washington DC?

The puzzles begin overleaf. You must open the doors in the correct sequence. When you have found the solution to each door you may advance through to the next. Keep track of your progress in the grid above. Remember, fail to solve just one puzzle and you put the sanity of the President and the health of America at risk.

Your 120 minutes begin NOW!

Test 1

(Solve to open door 1)
Which two grapefruit slices do not go with the other ten?

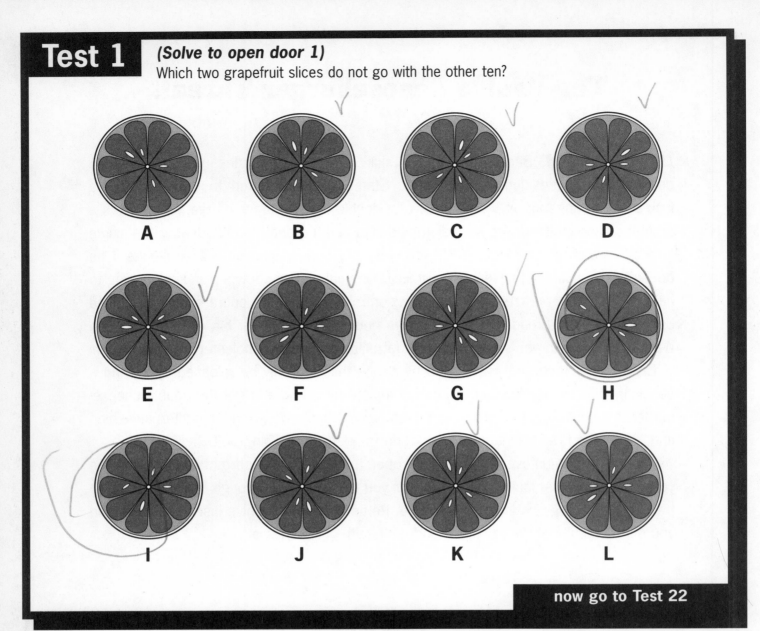

A   B   C   D

E   F   G   H

I   J   K   L

now go to Test 22

Test 2

(Solve to open door 20)
Which is the odd one out?

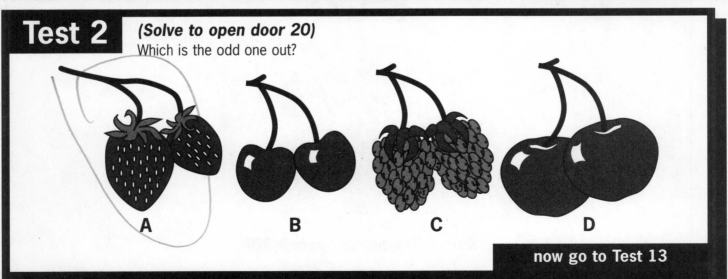

A   B   C   D

now go to Test 13

(Solve to open door 7)
What fruit should replace the question mark, A, B or C?

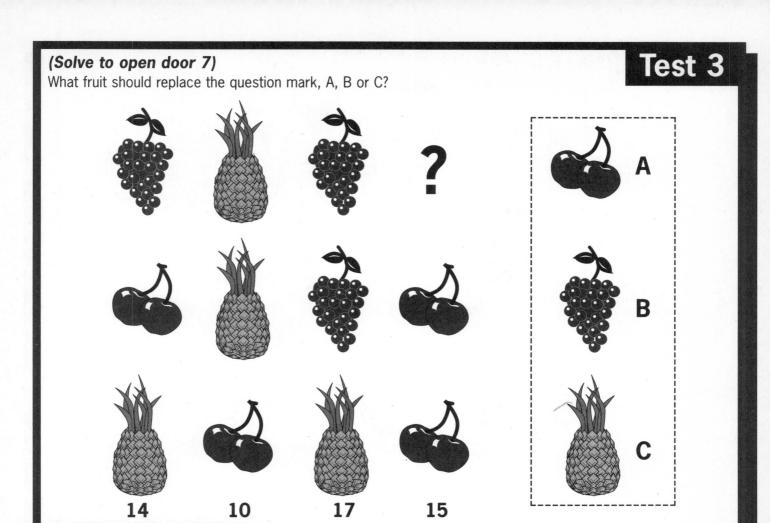

14   10   17   15

now go to Test 15

(Solve to open door 25)
What cauliflower comes next?

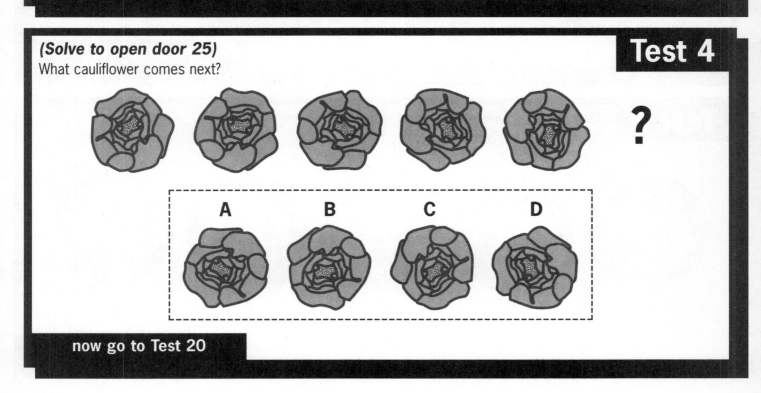

now go to Test 20

Test 5

(*Solve to open door 12*)
Complete the analogy.

 is to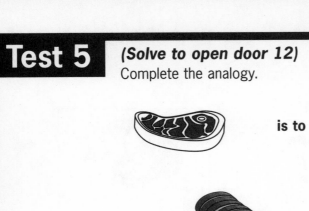

 as 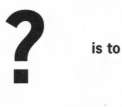 **?** is to

A 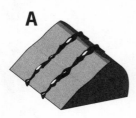 **B** 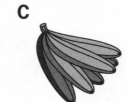 **C**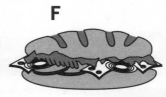

D  **E**  **F**

now go to Test 8

Test 6

(*Solve to open door 6*)
Which is the odd one out?

A   **B**   **C**   **D**   **E**

now go to Test 3

(Solve to open door 4)
Draw four straight lines to make eight sections which have in each section 3 sausages and respectively 8, 7, 6, 5, 4, 3, 2, and 1 pears.

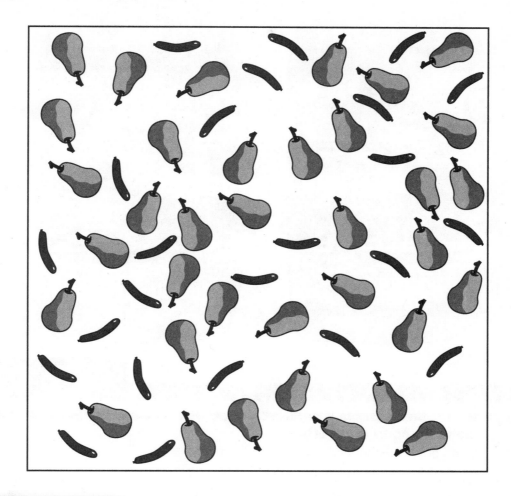

now go to Test 14

(Solve to open door 13)
Which is the odd one out?

A   B   C   D

now go to Test 17

61

Test 9

(Solve to open door 18)

What are the 15 differences in picture B?

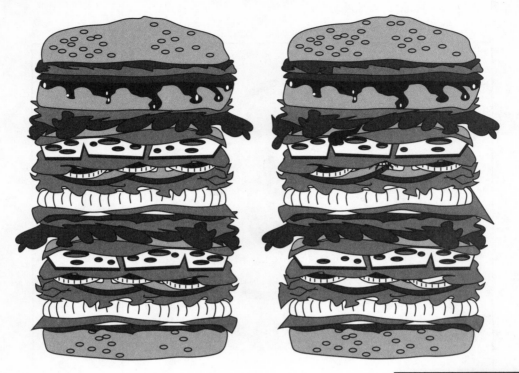

A

B

now go to Test 21

Test 10

(Solve to open door 10)

What comes next in this series?

   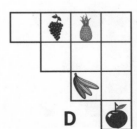

A   B   C   D

now go to Test 16

(Solve to open door 23)

All the oranges plus all the bunches of grapes are worth 18. All the oranges minus all the bunches of grapes are worth 12. If there were four times as many pairs of cherries, and twice as many oranges, the value of all the pairs of cherries would be the same as the value of all the oranges. What is the pair of cherries worth?

now go to Test 24

(Solve to open door 15)

Complete the analogy.

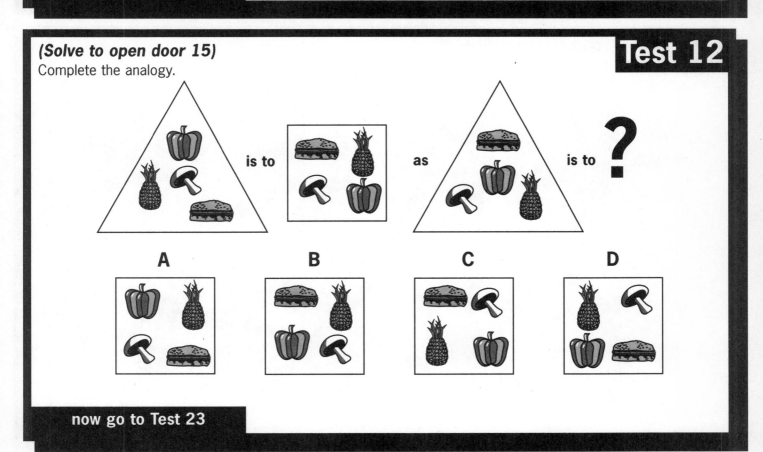

now go to Test 23

Test 13

Test 13 (Solve to open door 21)
Which set of parts fits perfectly into the joint of meat on the left to make a complete joint?

A

B

C

D

E

now go to Test 26

Test 14

(Solve to open door 5)
Which is the odd one out?

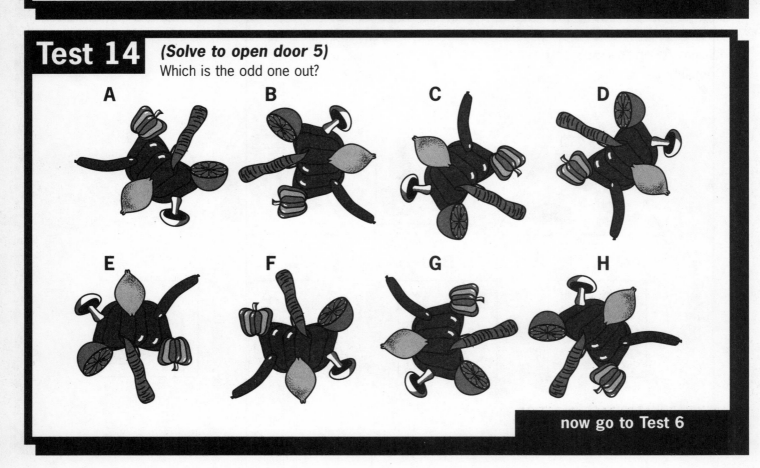

A   B   C   D

E   F   G   H

now go to Test 6

64

(Solve to open door 8)
Which set should replace the question mark to complete the pattern?

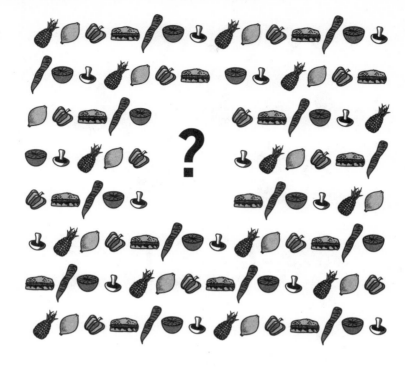

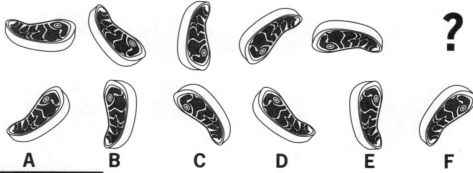

now go to Test 18

(Solve to open door 11)
Which salmon steak comes next?

A   **B**   **C**   **D**   **E**   **F**

now go to Test 5

Test 17

(Solve to open door 14)
What should replace the question mark?

$$\therefore 4 \times \text{(goblet)} + \text{(pie)} = 3 \times \text{(ice cream)} - ?$$

A (goblet) B (lime) C (worm) D (ice cream) E (pie)

now go to Test 12

Test 18

(Solve to open door 9)
How many apples are missing from this display?

now go to Test 10

(Solve to open door 17)
Which is the odd one out?

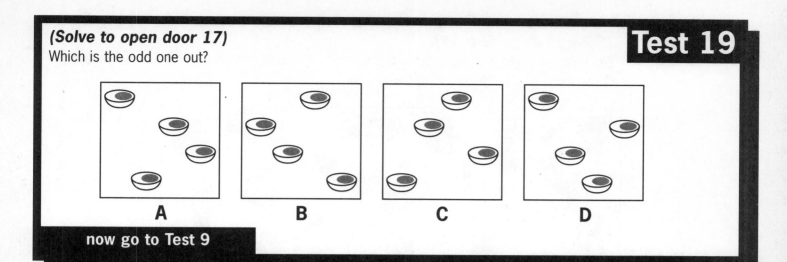

A   B   C   D

now go to Test 9

(Solve to open door 26 – the final door)
This system of levers and rollers is in balance. The black points are fixed swivel points. The shaded points are non-fixed swivel points. If a pie is placed at A, will the pie at B go up or go down?

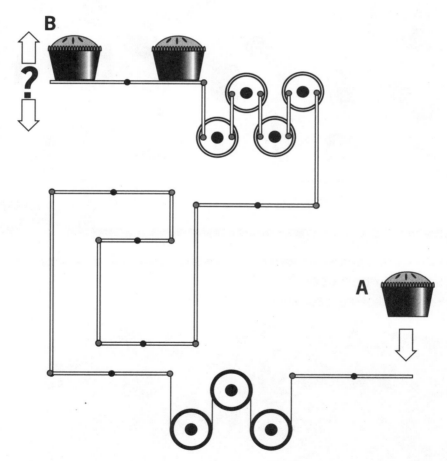

Now give the President his double cheeseburger on rye, but be careful, he is ravenously hungry. Watch your fingers!

Test 21

(Solve to open door 19)

Draw four straight lines that divide this display into four sections which have, respectively, 3, 4, 5 and 6 of each item in each section.

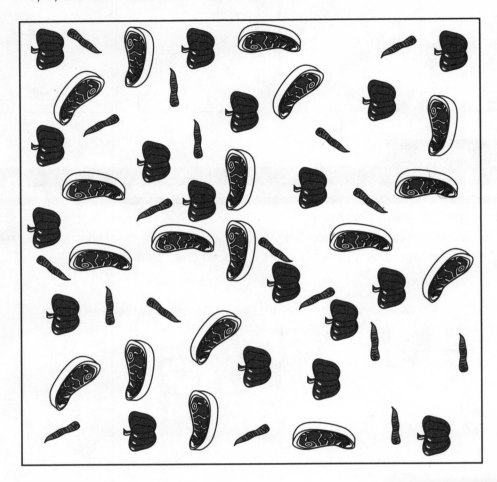

now go to Test 2

Test 22

(Solve to open door 2)

How many hot-dog sausages are in this display?

123

now go to Test 25

Test 23

(Solve to open door 16)
Which is the odd one out?

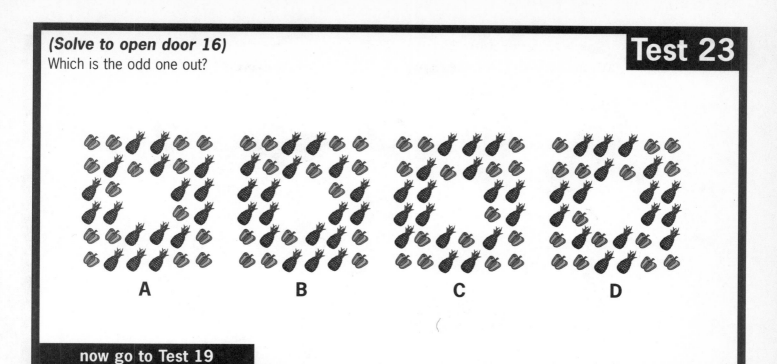

A   **B**   **C**   **D**

now go to Test 19

Test 24

(Solve to open door 24)
This system is not in balance, but is being held in position by the chain C. A and B are swivel points. Draw the position where the additional barrel of apples should be placed to return the system to balance, allowing the chain to be removed.

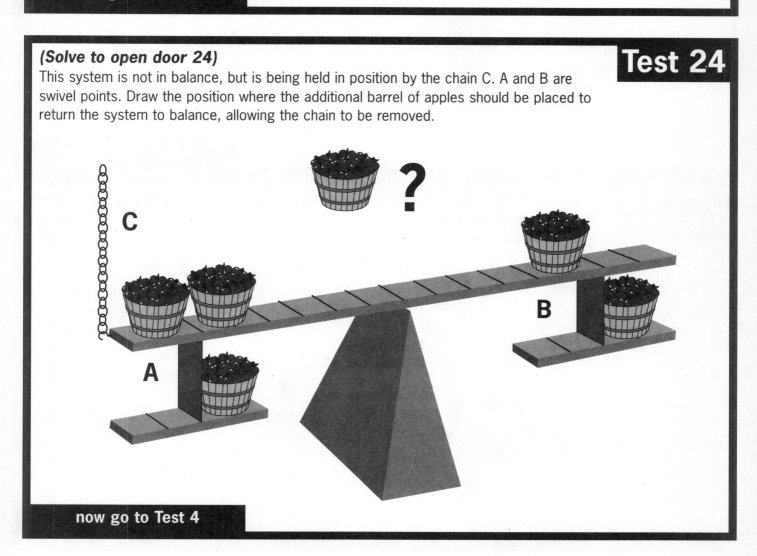

now go to Test 4

Test 25

(Solve to open door 3)
Which sandwich comes next?

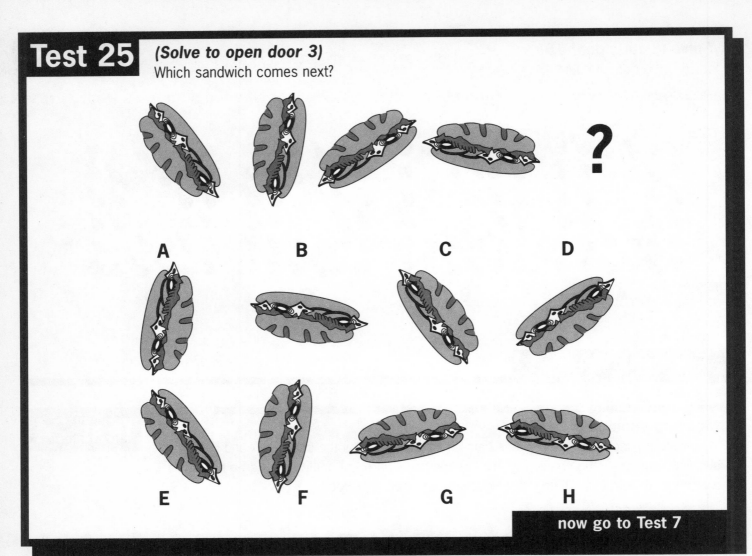

A **B** **C** **D**

E **F** **G** **H**

now go to Test 7

Test 26

(Solve to open door 22)
Which is the odd one out?

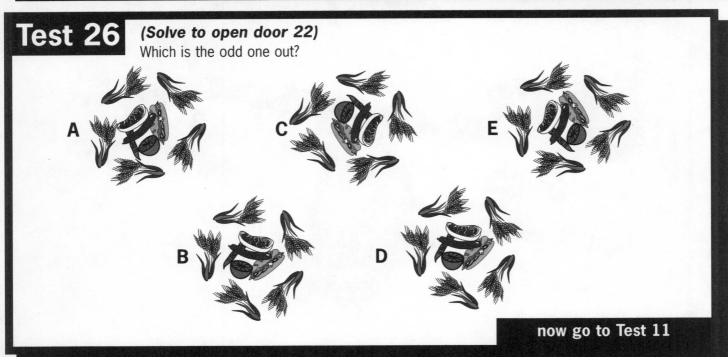

now go to Test 11

1. H and I. The seeds are in different relative positions.

2. A. The stalks of the strawberry is different to the other.

3. B. Cherry = 4; grape = 7; pineapple = 3.

4. C. The cabbages rotate clockwise.

5. D. Bread comes from wheat as steak comes from cattle.

6. A. The white icing changes its relative position.

7.

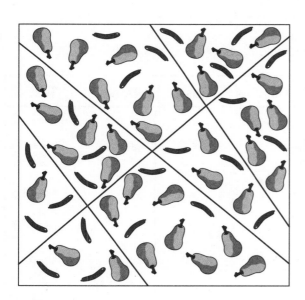

8. D. This is a mirror image reversal of the arrangement of the other apples.

9. *see next column*

10. A. The sequence rotates clockwise 2 steps at a time.

11. 7.5. Oranges = 5, grapes = 1.5.

9.

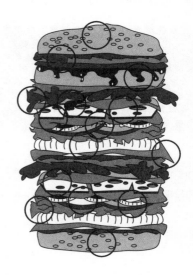

12. D. The objects move as follows: top to bottom-right; middle to bottom-left; bottom-right to top-left; bottom-left to top-right.

13. A.

14. B. The sausage is bent toward the lemon.

15. D. Each row advances by 3.

16. C. The steaks rotate clockwise, one-eighth of a turn (45°).

17. C. Values double in the following order; egg, orange slice, prawns, cone, sandwich. If the relative values are 2, 4, 8, 16 and 32, the final sum would be (4 x 2) [8] + 32 [40] = (3 x 16) [48] – 8 = [40].

18. There are 53 apples missing.

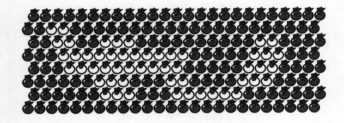

19. D. This is a mirror image reversal of the arrangement of the other eggs.

20. Down.

21.

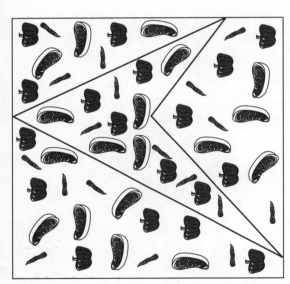

22. 84 sausages.

23. C. This is a mirror image reversal of the arrangement of the other displays.

24.

25. C. The sandwiches rotate clockwise one-eighth of a turn (45°).

26. A. The middle objects are in a different relative position to the outer ears of wheat.

You should have followed this route:

Door	Test	Door	Test
1	1	14	17
2	22	15	12
3	25	16	23
4	7	17	19
5	14	18	9
6	6	19	21
7	3	20	2
8	15	21	13
9	18	22	26
10	10	23	11
11	16	24	24
12	5	25	4
13	8	26	20

Find the only continuous route from the left of this puzzle to the right.

100

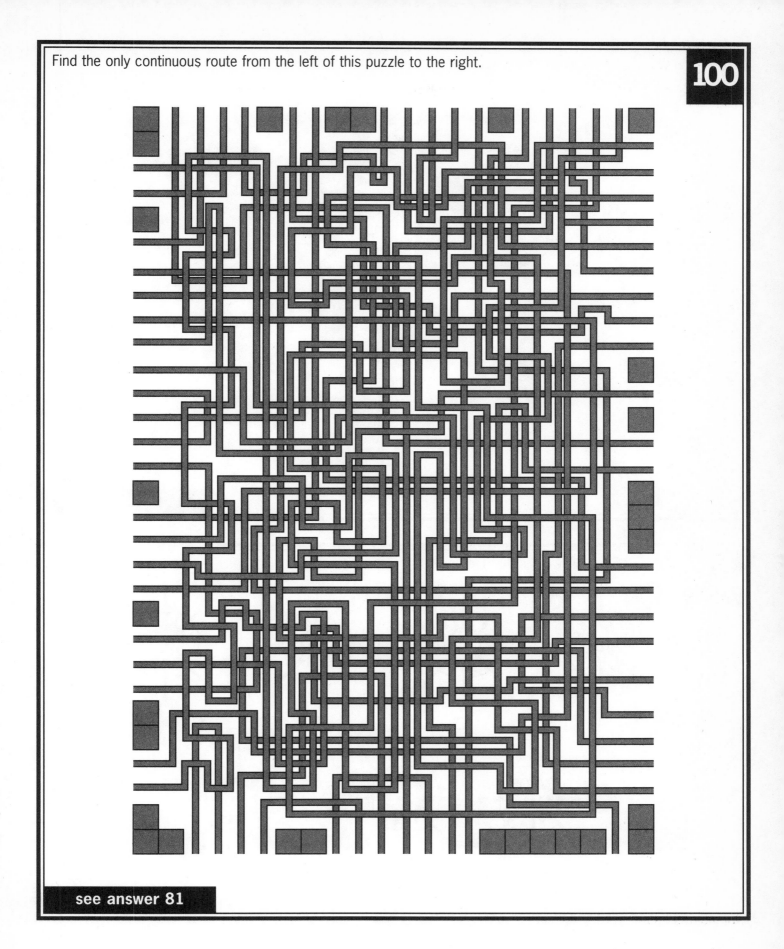

see answer 81

101

Which of the surrounding pieces fits perfectly on top of the middle piece to make a rectangular block?

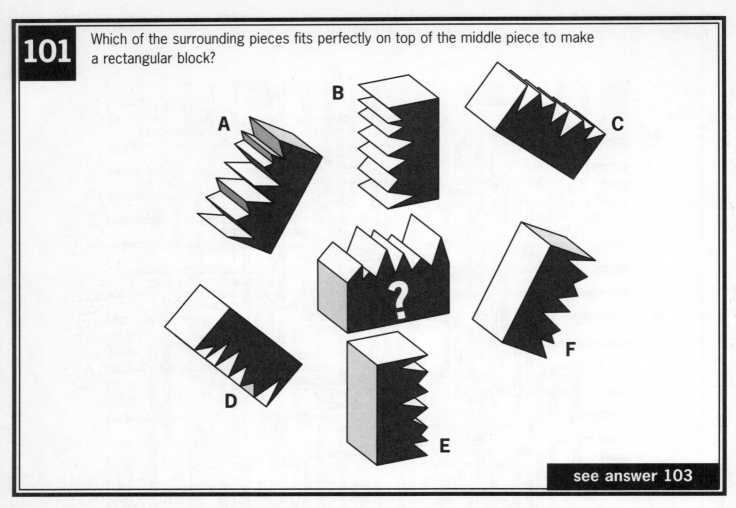

see answer 103

102

Which of the following is the odd one out?

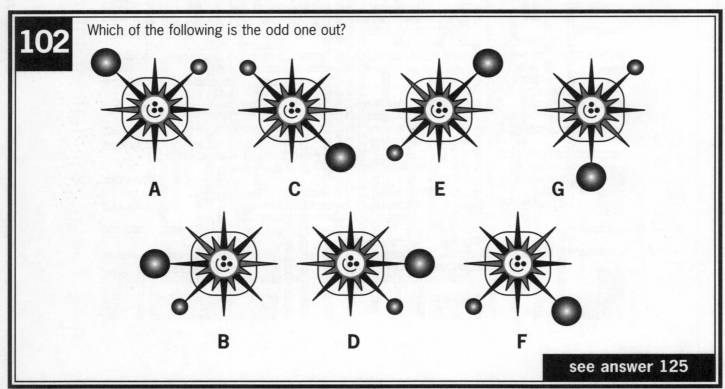

A   C   E   G

B   D   F

see answer 125

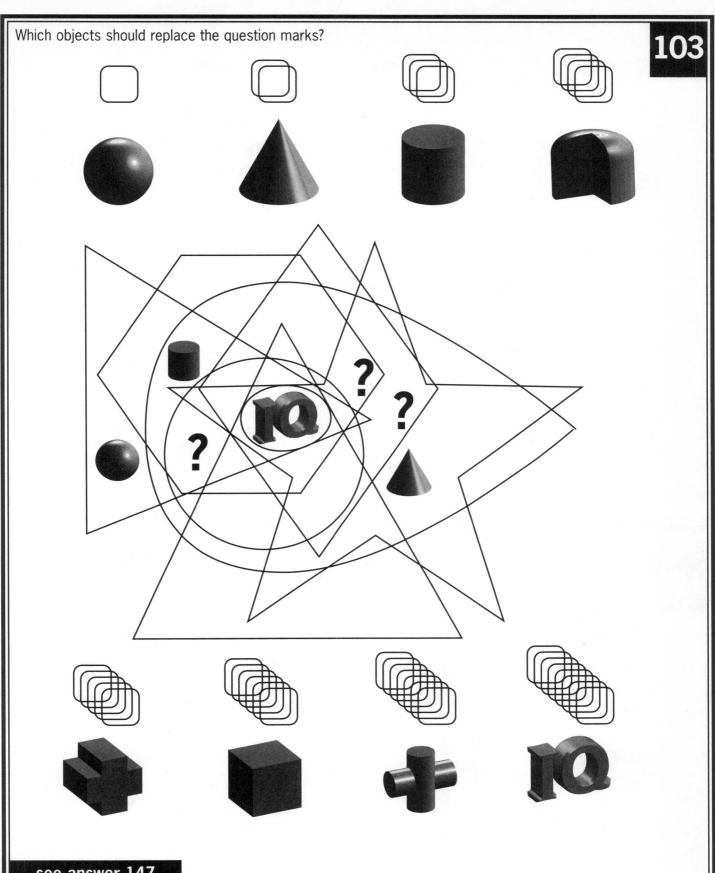

see answer 147

104 Which of the surrounding shapes is the box in the middle opened out?

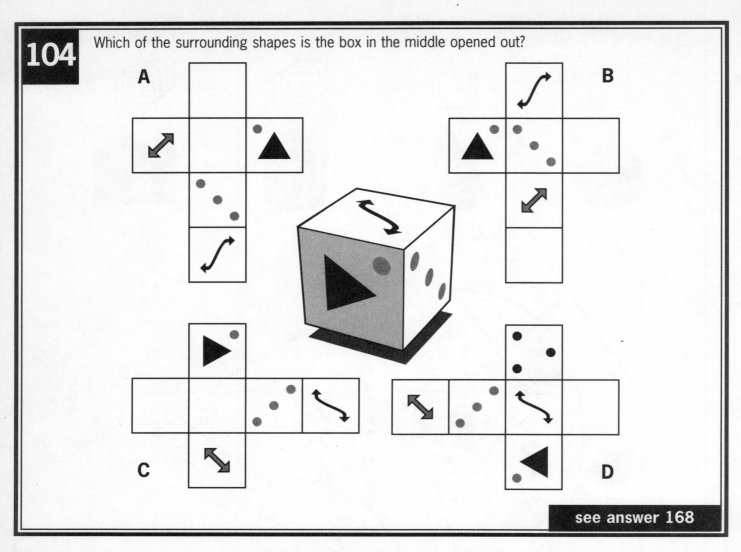

see answer 168

105 Complete the analogy.

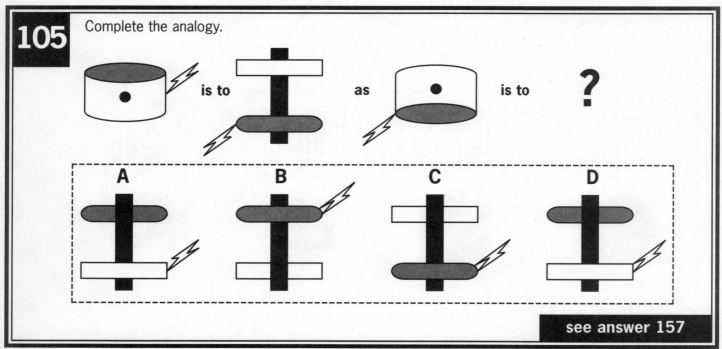

is to   as   is to   **?**

A   B   C   D

see answer 157

Which of the following is the odd one out?

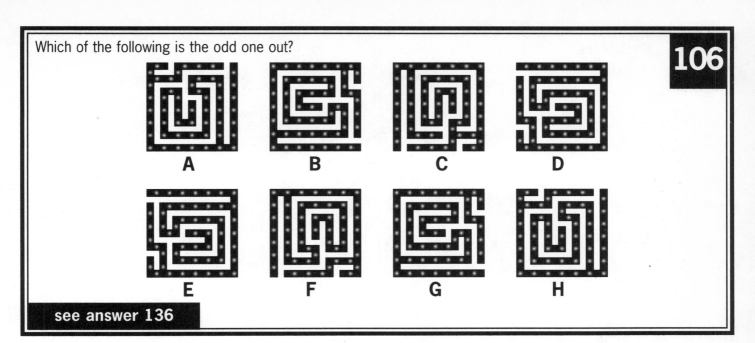

A   B   C   D

E   F   G   H

see answer 136

In this system of pulley wheels and levers, where the black spots are fixed pivots and the shaded spots are non-fixed pivots, will (A) rise or fall and will (B) rise or fall when the wheel at the top is turned in the direction indicated.

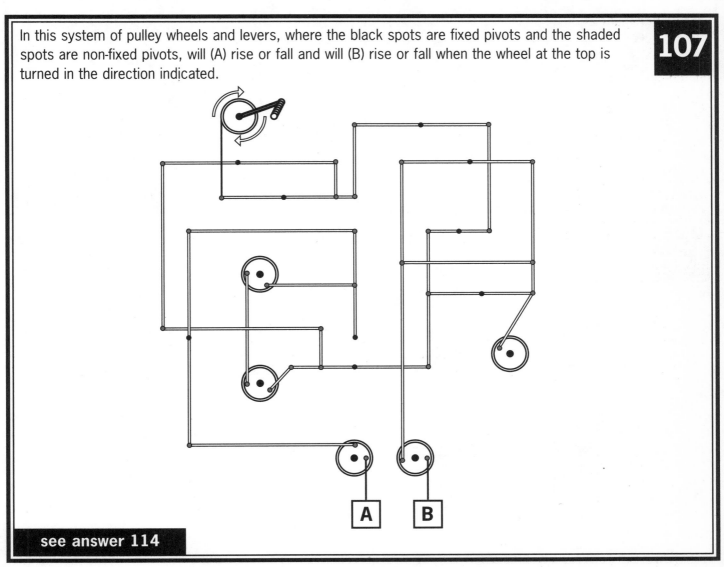

see answer 114

108

Which of the figures below is the same as the one in the box?

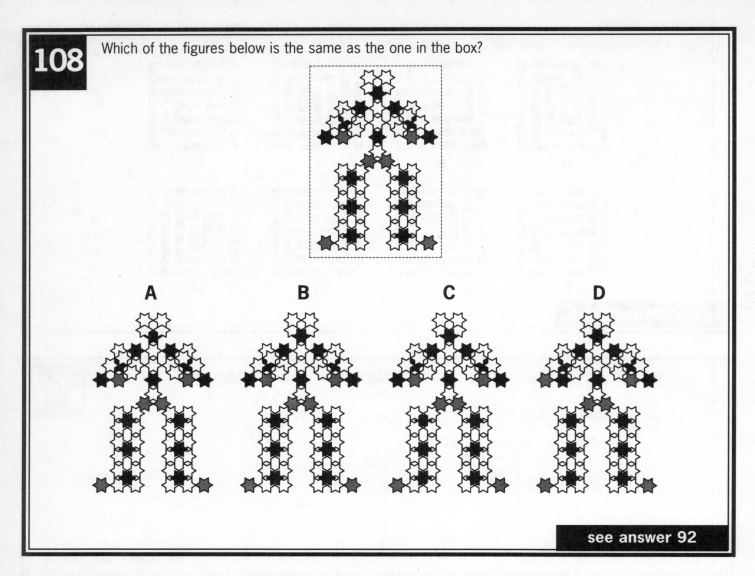

A   B   C   D

see answer 92

109

Which of the following is the odd one out?

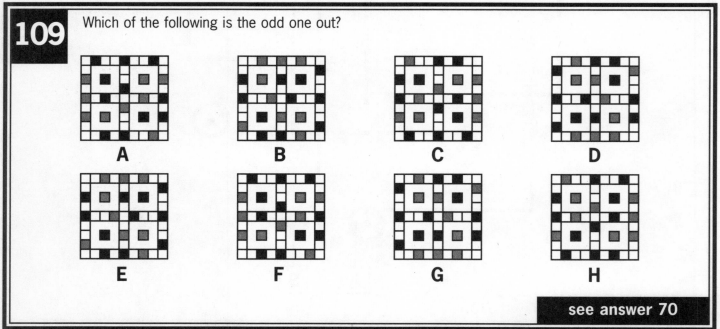

A   B   C   D

E   F   G   H

see answer 70

Draw five straight lines that divide this puzzle into six sections that have 1 chimp, 1 koala, 3 snakes, 4 dogs and 5 stars in each section. The lines do not have to go from one edge to another.

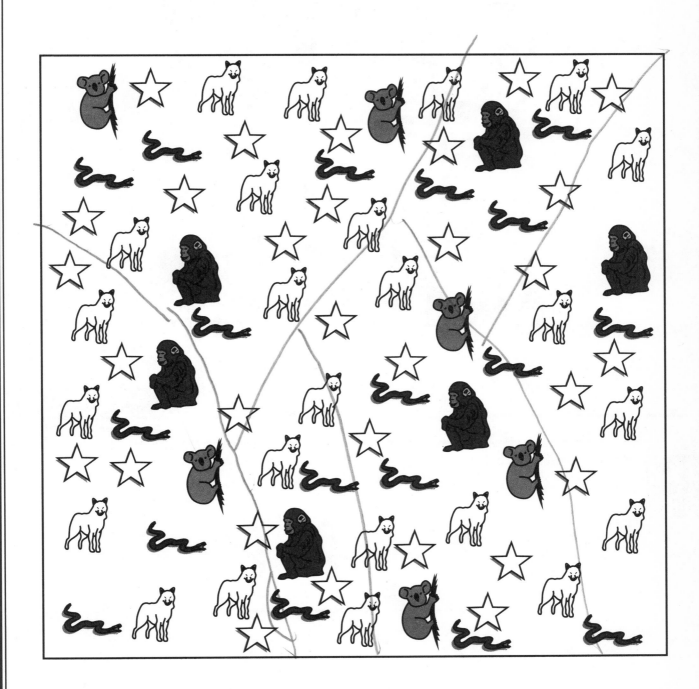

see answer 49

111

Which of the following is the odd one out?

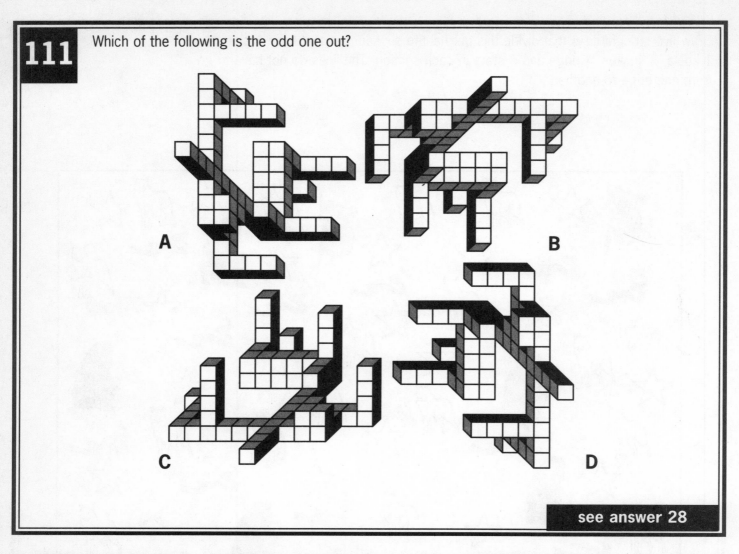

A

B

C

D

see answer 28

112

Which of the figures below should replace the question mark the box?

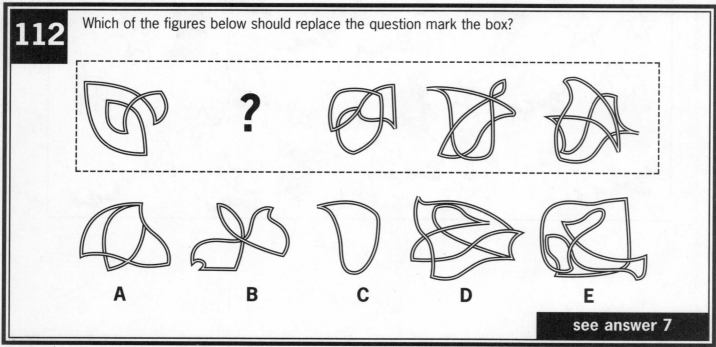

?

A   B   C   D   E

see answer 7

Complete the analogy?

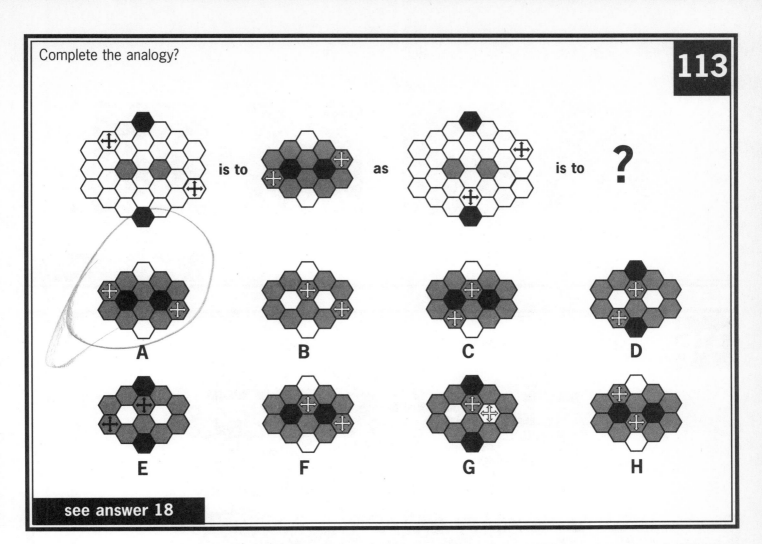

A   B   C   D

E   F   G   H

see answer 18

A black block below weighs three times a white block. Where should one black box be placed to return this system to balance?

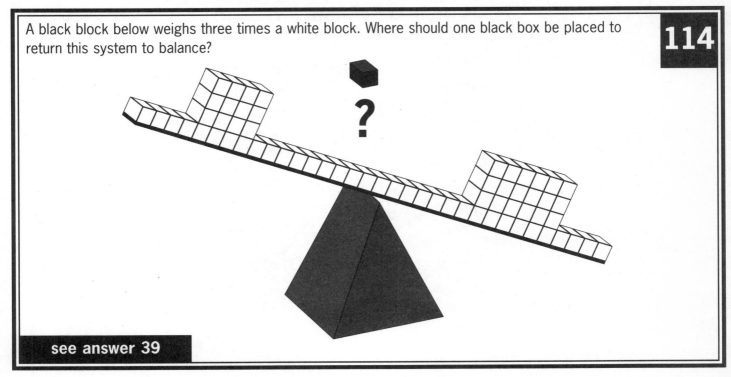

see answer 39

115

Which of the following is the odd one out?

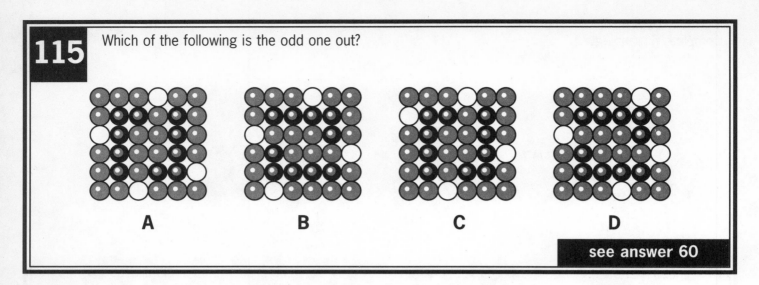

A   B   C   D

see answer 60

116

Find the 10 horse & carriage sets hidden behind these vehicles.

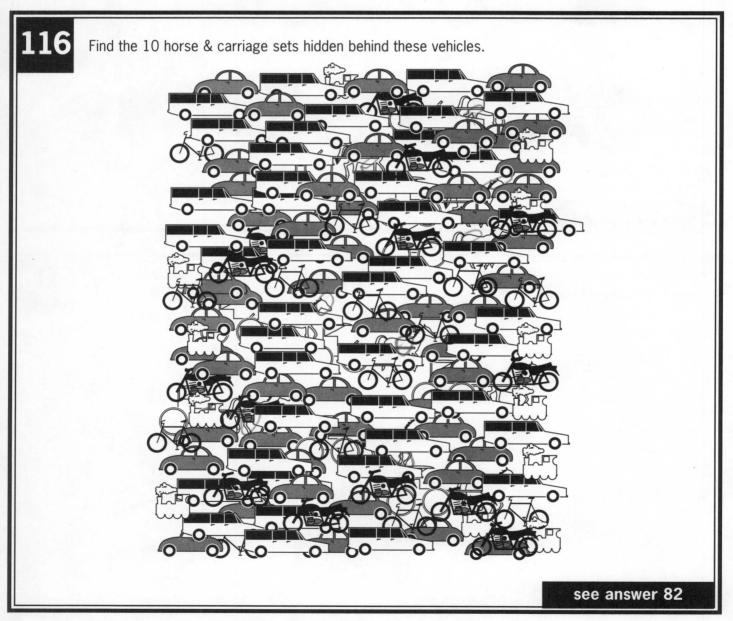

see answer 82

A

B

C

D

see answer 104

118 What comes next in this series?

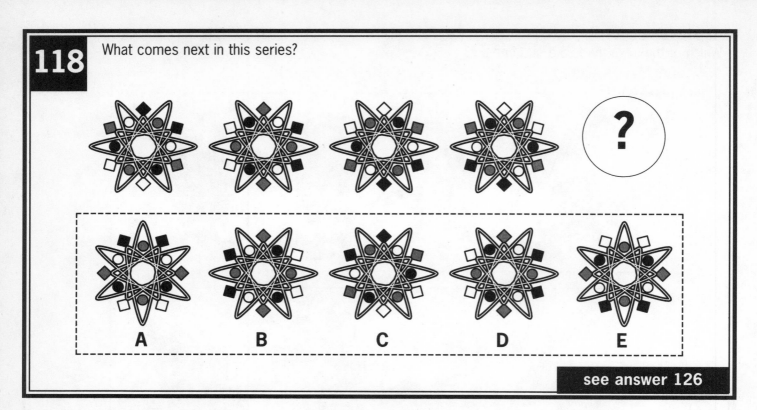

A   B   C   D   E

see answer 126

119 What would this pyramid look like opened out?

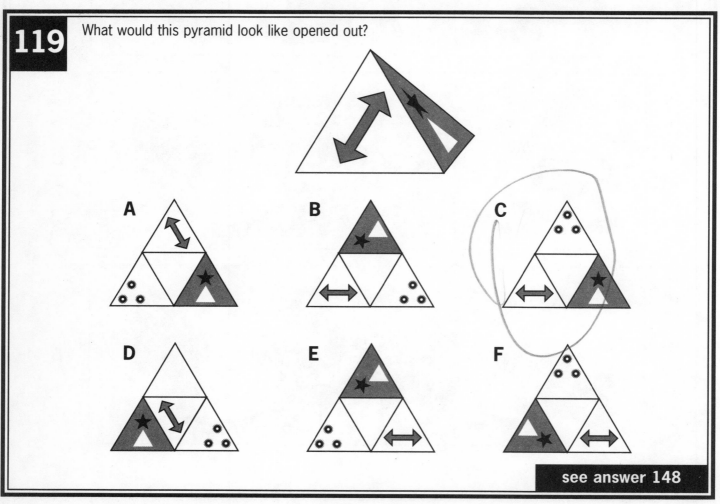

A   B   C

D   E   F

see answer 148

In this system of cogs, levers and pulley wheels, in which the black spots are fixed pivot points and the shaded spots are non-fixed pivot points, the loads at A and B are in balance. Which one will rise when the wheel at the bottom is turned as indicated?

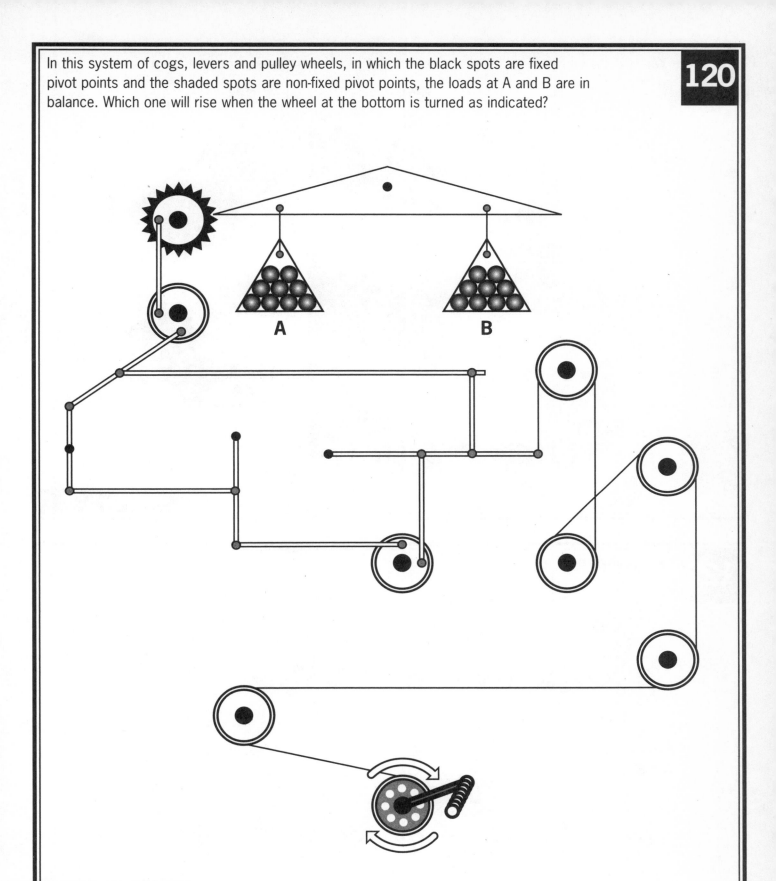

A

B

see answer 169

121

Which of the surrounding pieces fits perfectly on top of the middle piece to make a rectangular block.

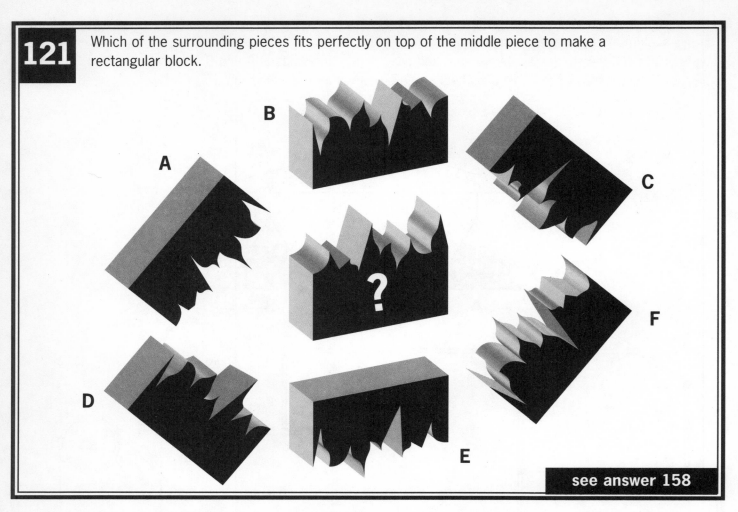

see answer 158

122

What comes next in this series?

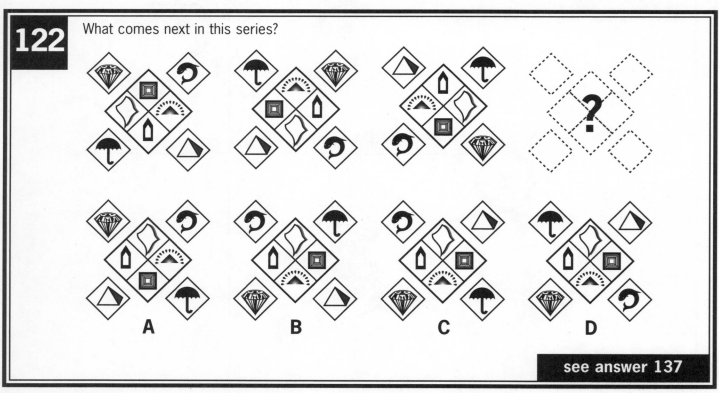

A   B   C   D

see answer 137

Which tile is missing from this series of panels?

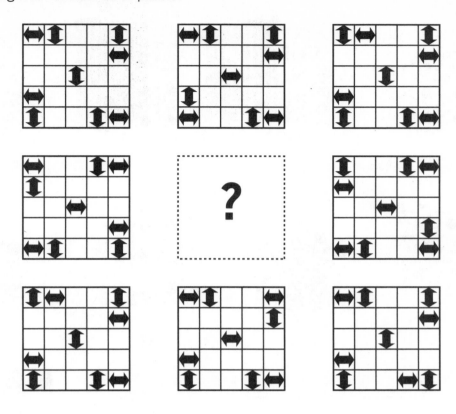

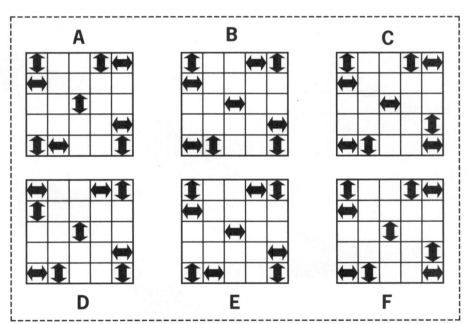

see answer 115

124 Which of the following is the odd one out?

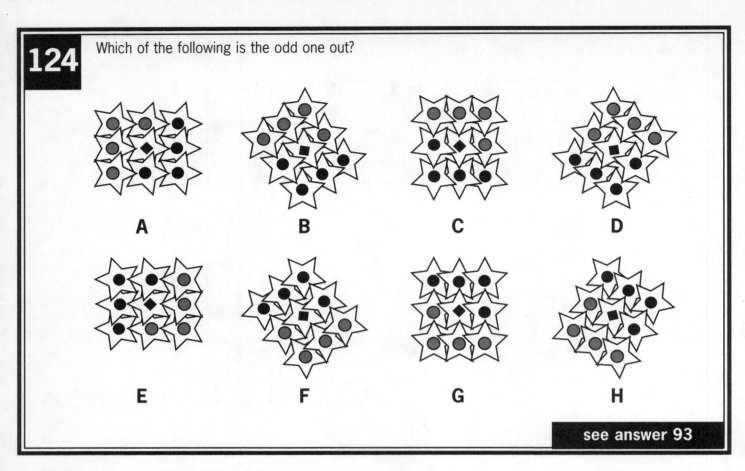

A B C D

E F G H

see answer 93

125 Which two of these images are identical?

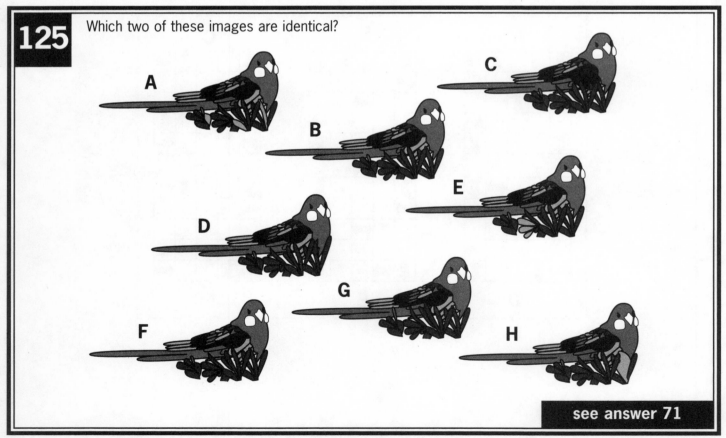

A

C

B

E

D

G

F

H

see answer 71

Find the 15 differences in picture B.

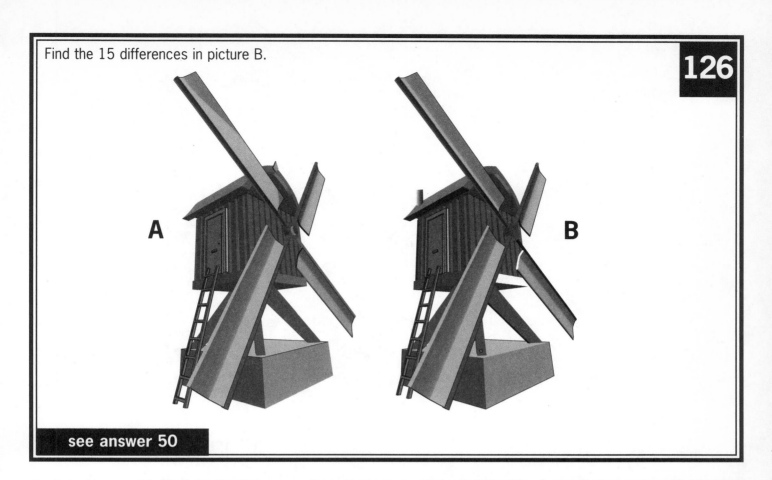

A   B

see answer 50

What is the missing set?

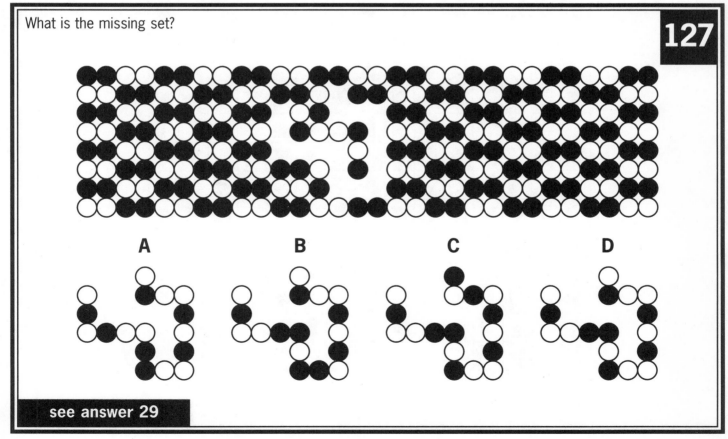

A   B   C   D

see answer 29

128 Map out the route to the diamond using the key below. Follow the direction of the apex of the triangle; for example the triangle to the right of Start is pointing right, so you should go 6 squares right. You may travel forward, back, up or down, but not diagonally nor retrace your steps, although your path may criss-cross.

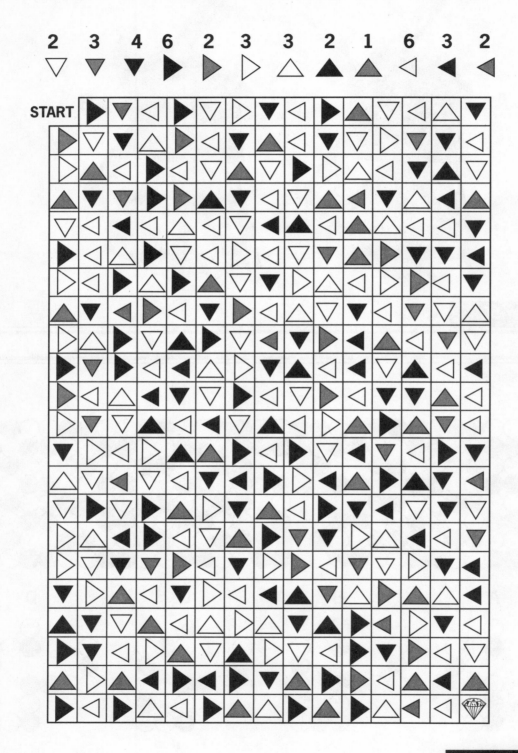

see answer 8

Draw three lines that connect the next three drums in sequence with the boxes they should go in.

129

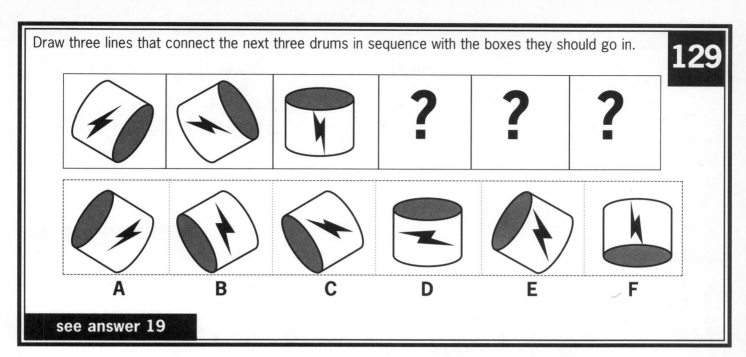

see answer 19

Which of the following is the odd one out?

130

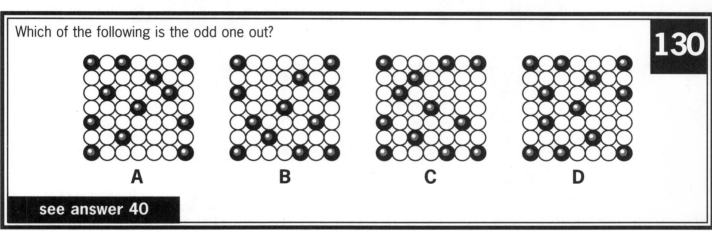

A B C D

see answer 40

Complete the analogy.

131

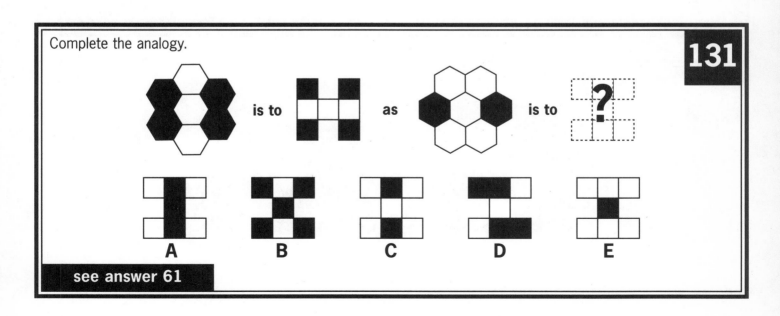

is to   as   is to   ?

A B C D E

see answer 61

132

What comes next in this series?

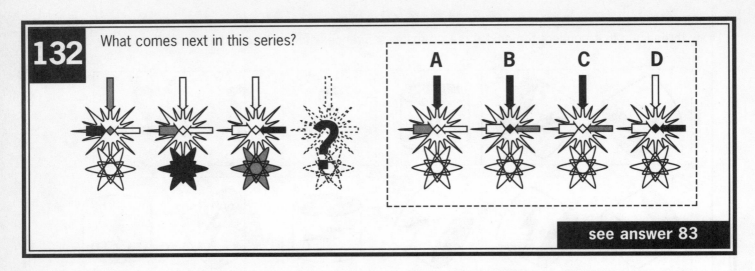

A B C D

see answer 83

133

What is the missing set?

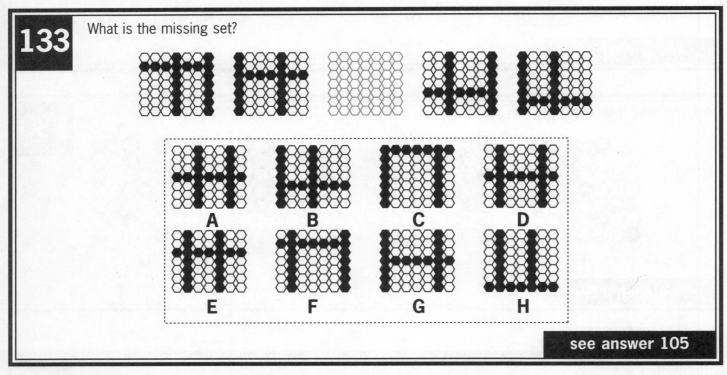

A   B   C   D

E   F   G   H

see answer 105

134

How many cobras are in this menacing group?

see answer 127

Draw three straight lines that make four sections with a total value of 40 in each, using the values given below. The lines do not have to go from one edge to another.

0   1   2   3   4   5

see answer 149

Which of the following is the odd one out?

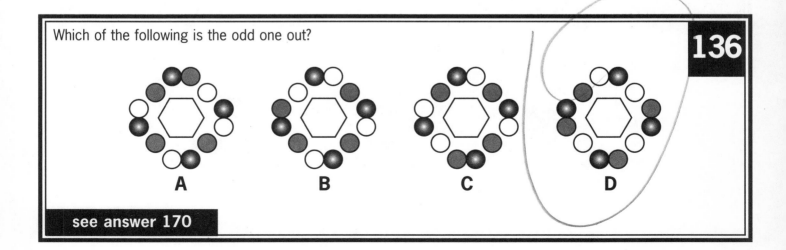

A   B   C   D

see answer 170

137

Which of the following is the odd one out?

A   B   C   D

E   F   G   H

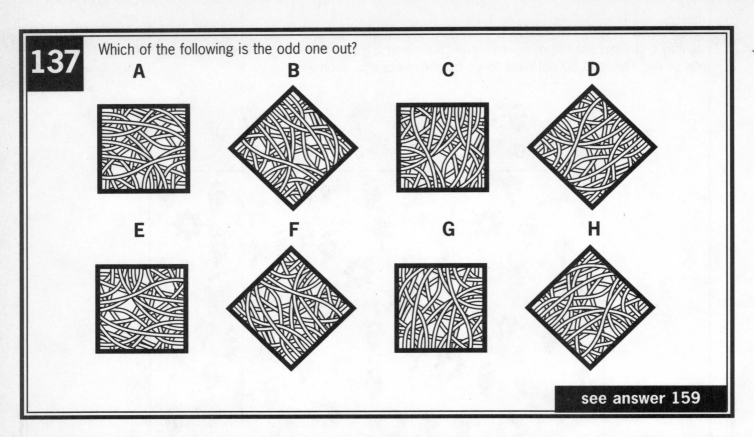

see answer 159

138

Which two do not go with the other four?

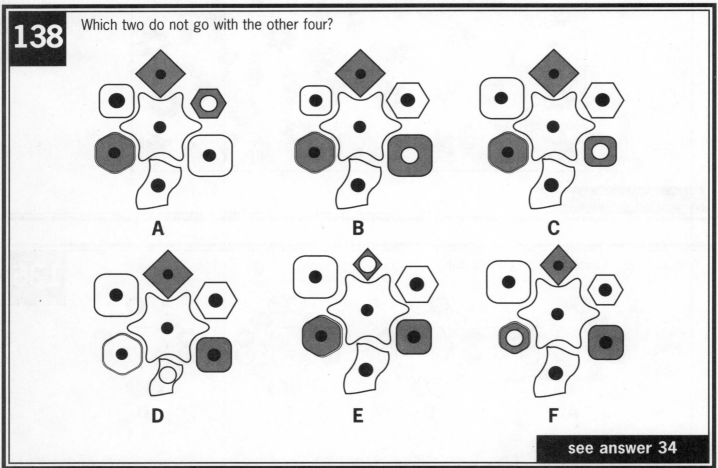

A   B   C

D   E   F

see answer 34

In this system of cogs, levers and rollers, in which the black spots are fixed swivel points and the shaded spots are non-fixed swivel points, does the load at A and the load at B rise or drop when the lever at the top is pushed as shown?

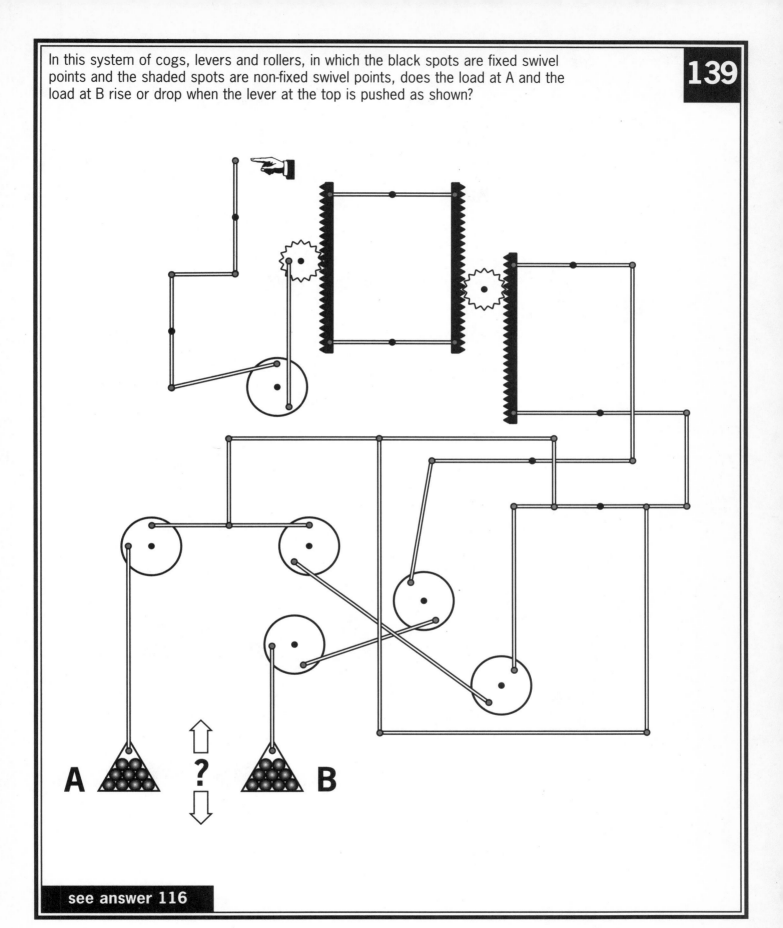

A ? B

see answer 116

Each like animal has the same value and the leopard, flea, dog and rabbit all have different values. Which of A, B, C, D, E or F is the total value of the single column above the question mark, and what are the lowest possible values of the animals?

see answer 94

Which of the following is the odd one out?

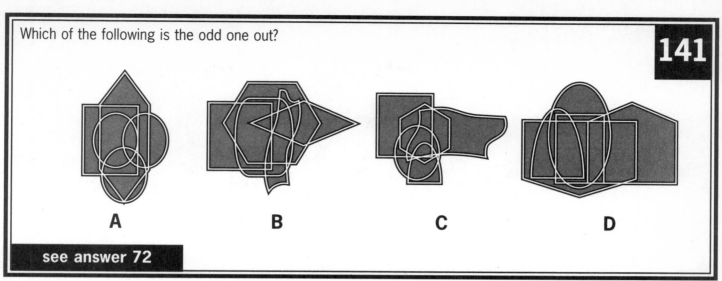

A　　　B　　　C　　　D

see answer 72

What are the 15 differences in picture B?

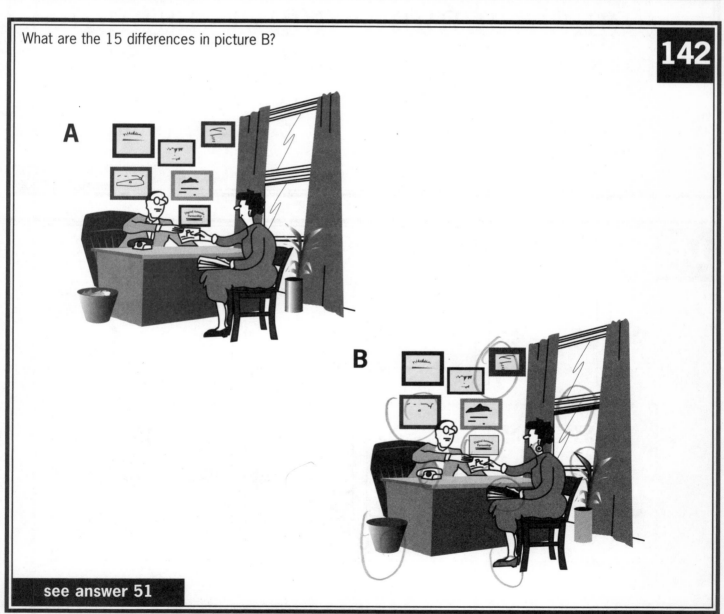

see answer 51

143 Complete the analogy.

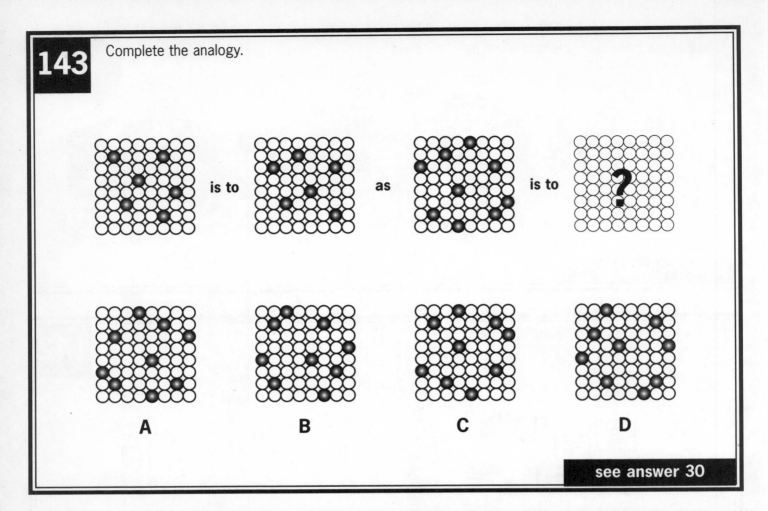

see answer 30

144 What comes next in this series?

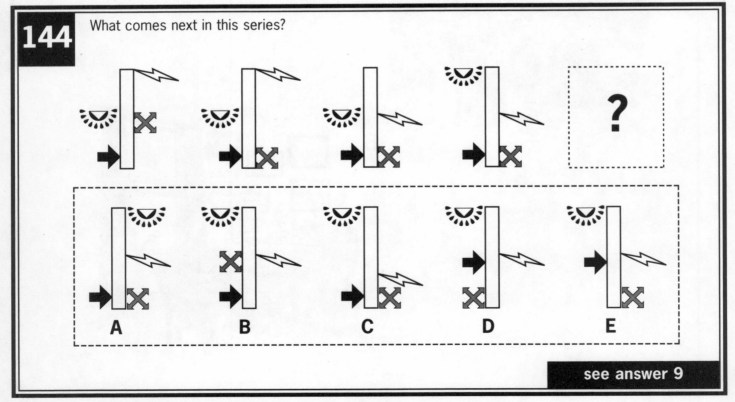

see answer 9

Find the only route from the perimeter of this field to the shaded path around the diamond.

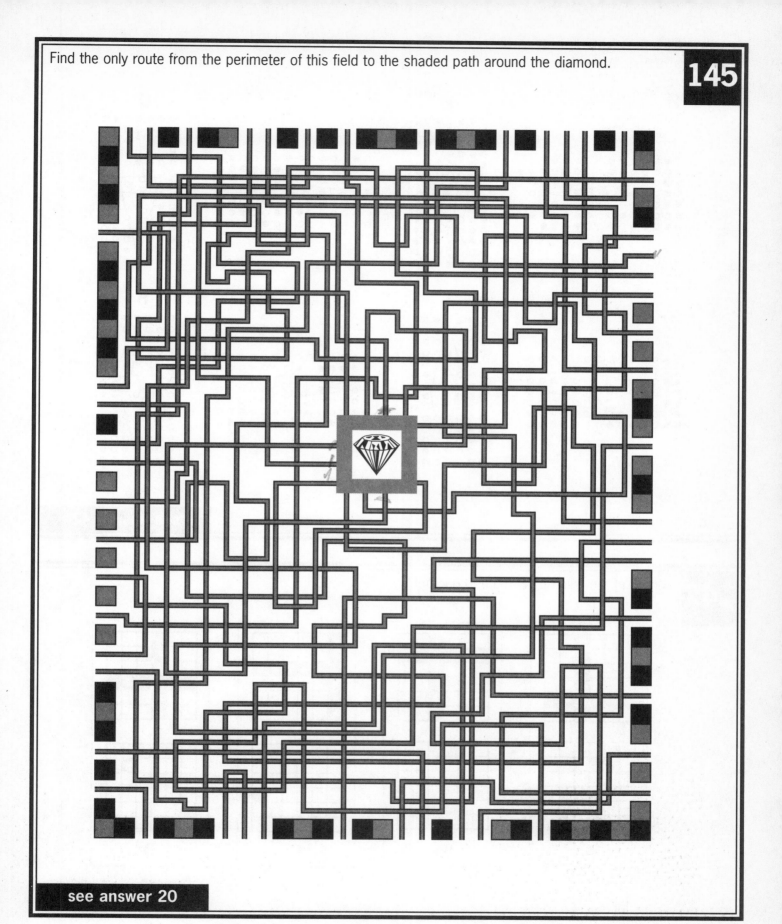

see answer 20

146

Find the odd one out in each row.

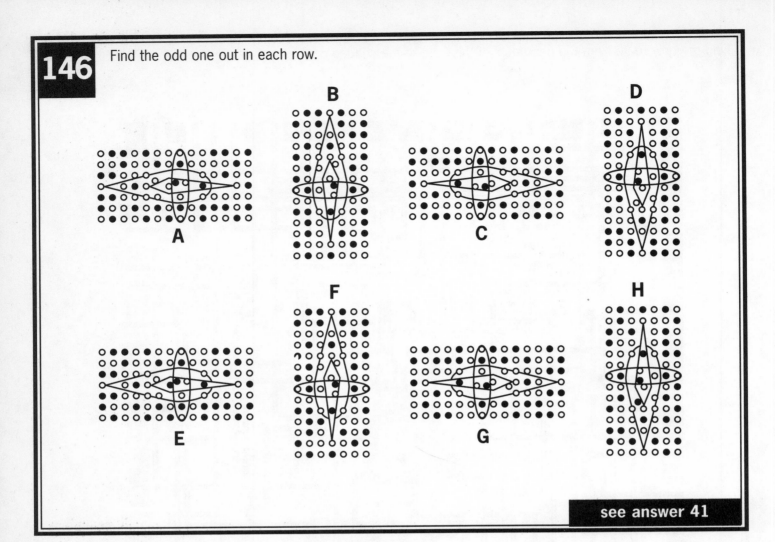

A B C D

E F G H

see answer 41

147

Which of the following is the odd one out?

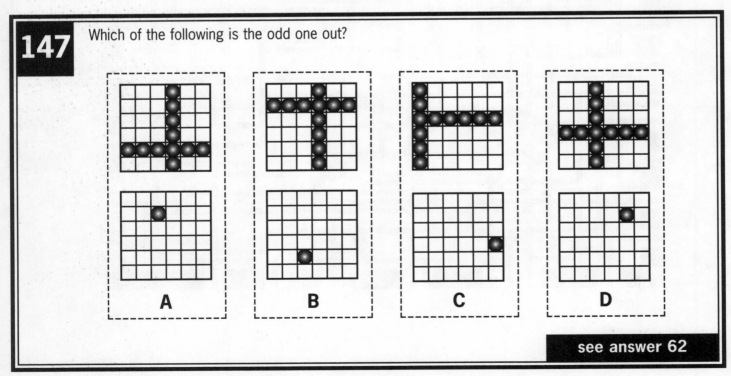

A B C D

see answer 62

Which is the missing panel?

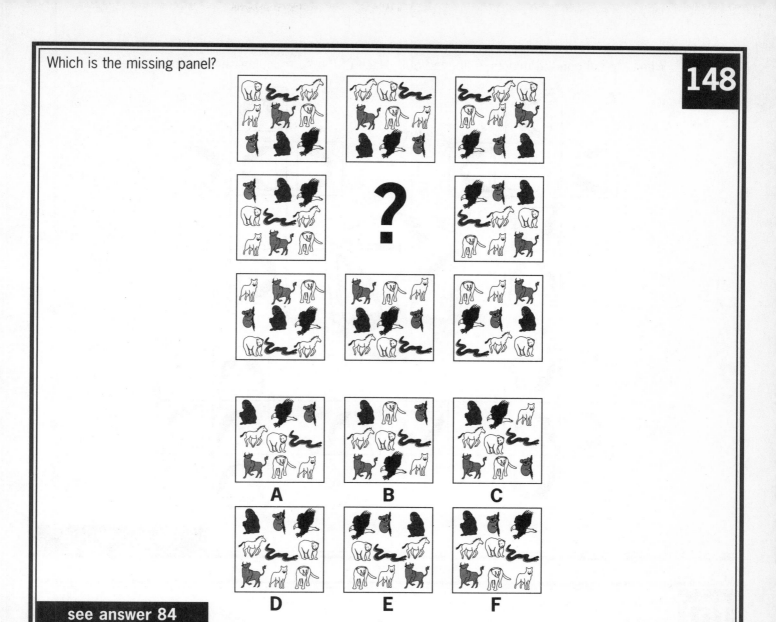

A   B   C

D   E   F

see answer 84

Which of the following is the odd one out?

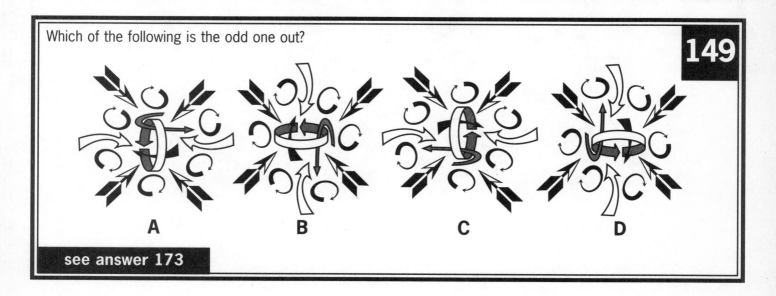

A   B   C   D

see answer 173

150

When the cube in the middle is opened out, which of the surrounding shapes does it make?

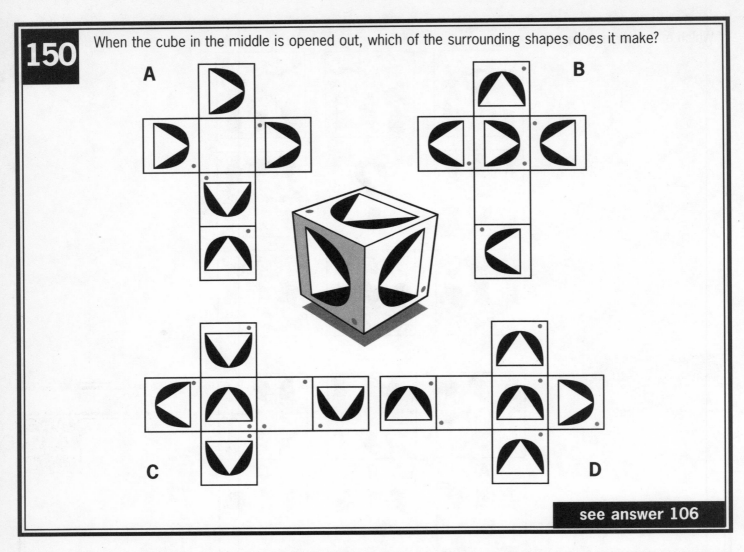

A

B

C

D

see answer 106

151

Complete the analogy.

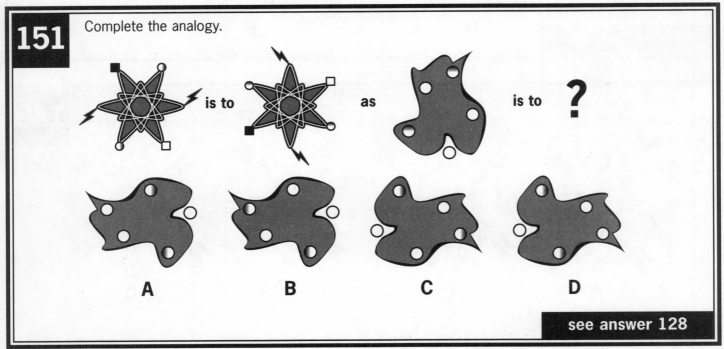

is to   as   is to   **?**

A   B   C   D

see answer 128

102

Which of the surrounding shapes fits exactly onto the middle piece to make a rectangular block?

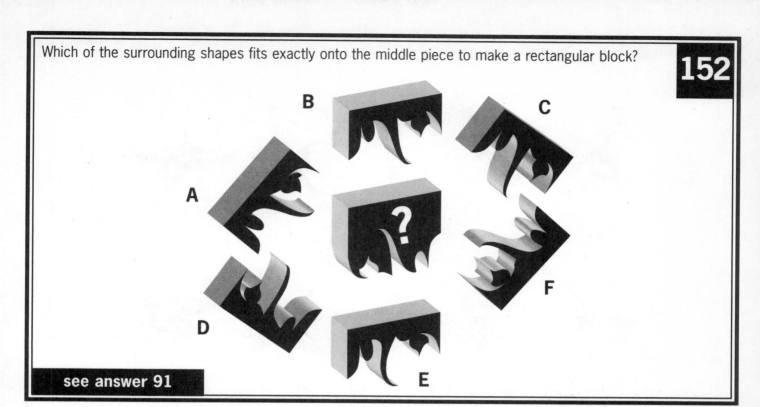

B

C

A

F

D

E

see answer 91

Which clock is the odd-one-out?

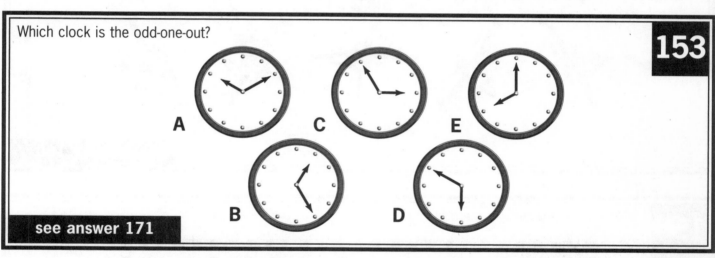

A

C

E

B

D

see answer 171

Which of the following is the odd one out?

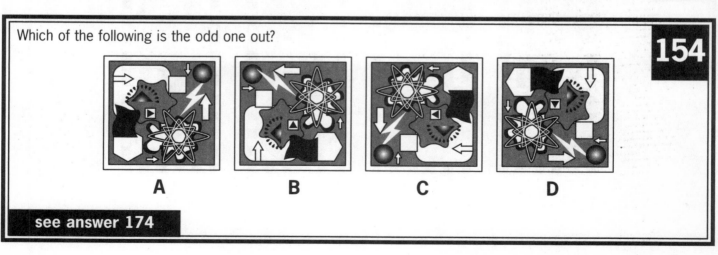

A

B

C

D

see answer 174

Which jet fighter is missing?

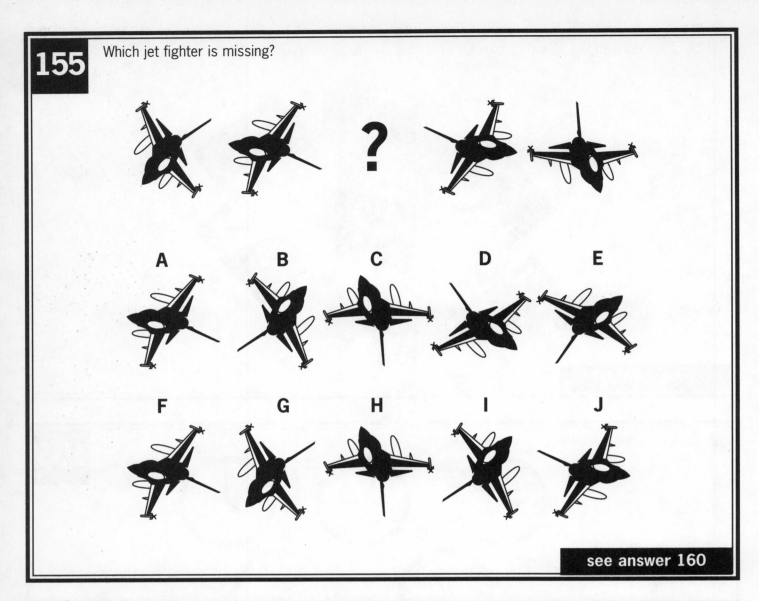

A   B   C   D   E

F   G   H   I   J

see answer 160

Which of the following is the odd one out?

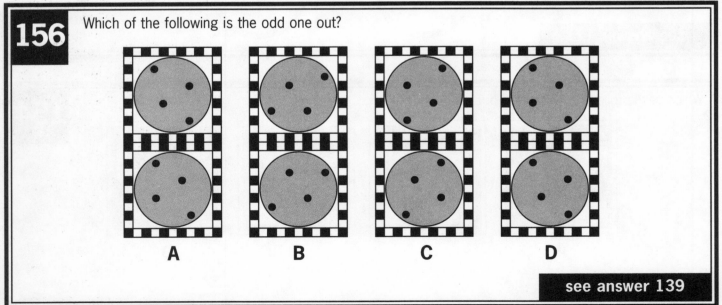

A   B   C   D

see answer 139

Which panel should replace the question mark?

157

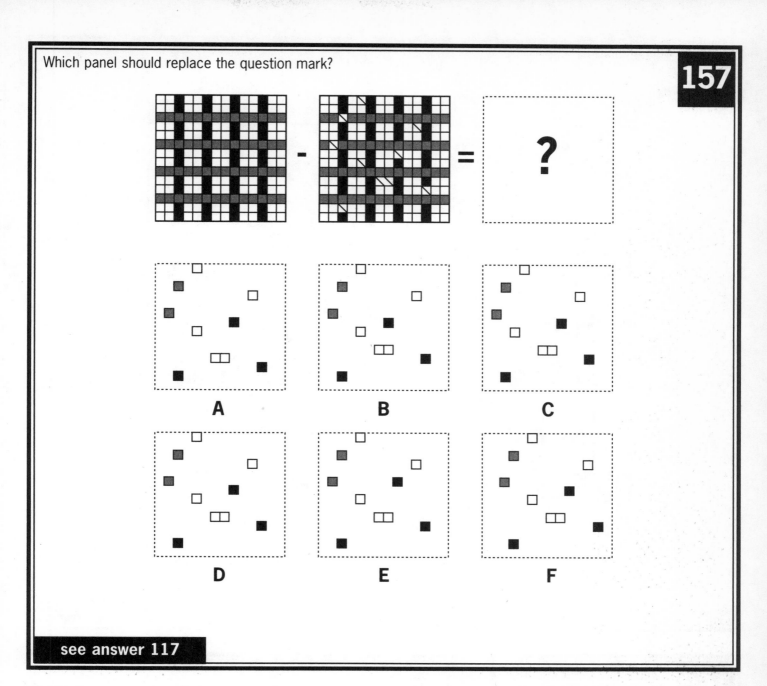

A B C

D E F

see answer 117

Which of the following is the odd one out?

158

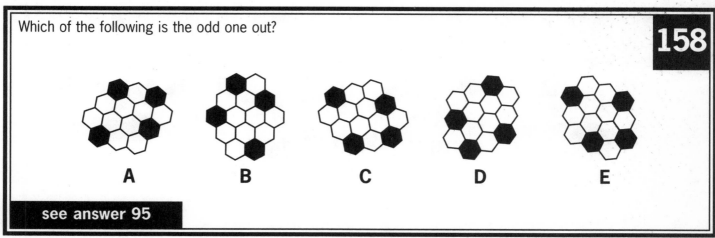

A B C D E

see answer 95

159

Draw four straight lines that divide this puzzle into five sections with 1 scuba diver, 3 fish and respectively, 4, 5, 6, 7 and 8 large bubbles and sea shells in each section. The lines do not have to go from one edge to another.

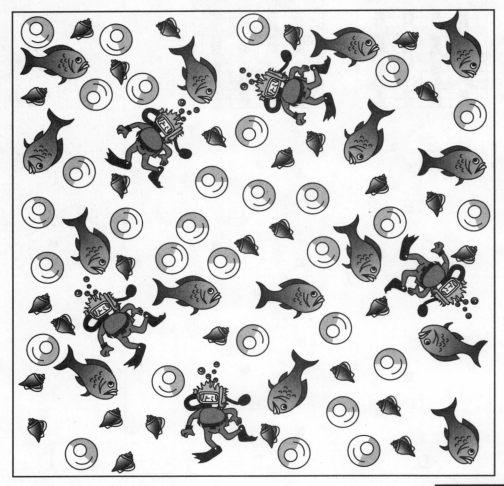

see answer 73

160

Which of the following is the odd one out?

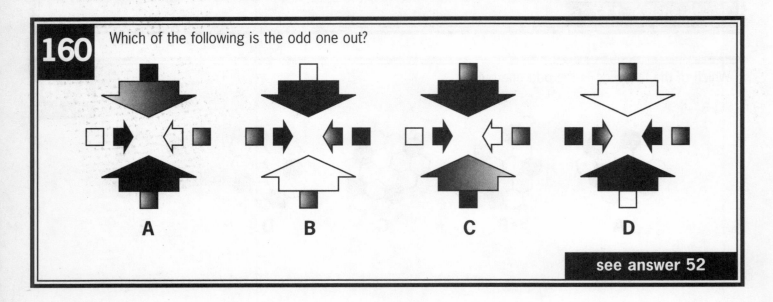

A   B   C   D

see answer 52

Which is the odd one out in each row?

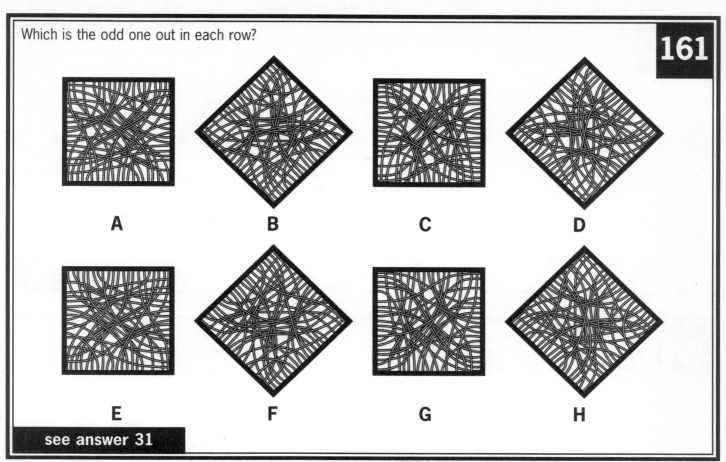

A   B   C   D

E   F   G   H

see answer 31

Which set fits into the middle of this set of tiles?

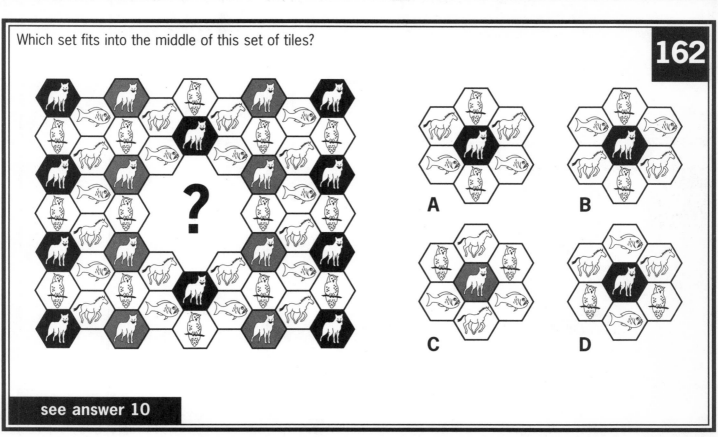

A   B

C   D

see answer 10

163 These ramps are fixed in position. When the ball at the top is released, where will it eventually come to rest?

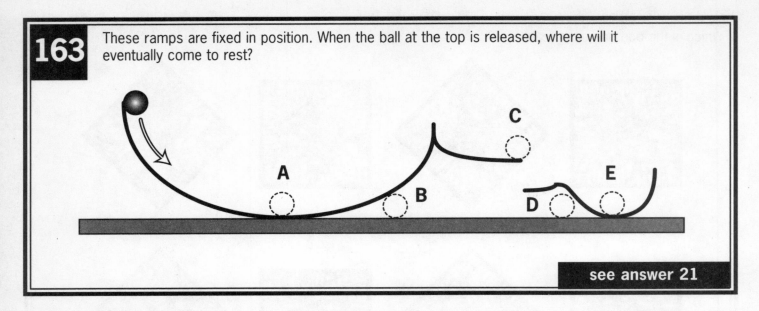

see answer 21

164 This system is in balance. The load at B is on a plank which sits on top of two rollers. The black spots are fixed pivot points and the white spots are non-fixed pivot points. When the lever at the bottom is pushed as shown, will the load at A rise or fall and will the load at B move left or right?

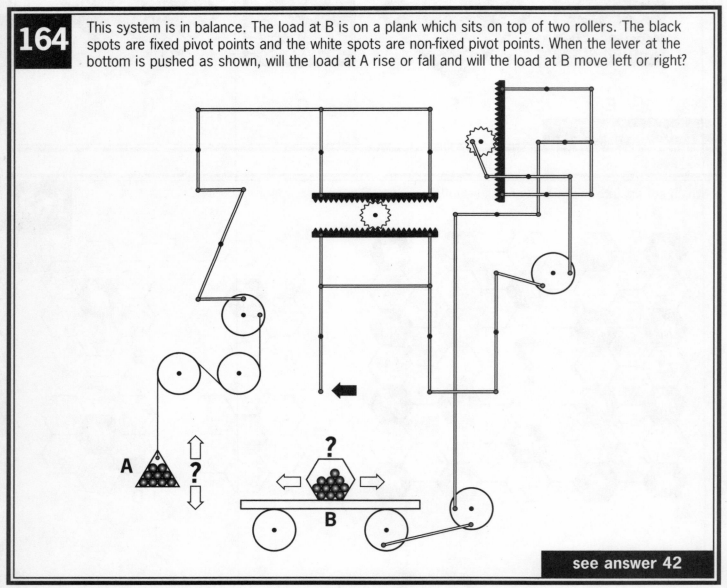

see answer 42

Complete the analogy.

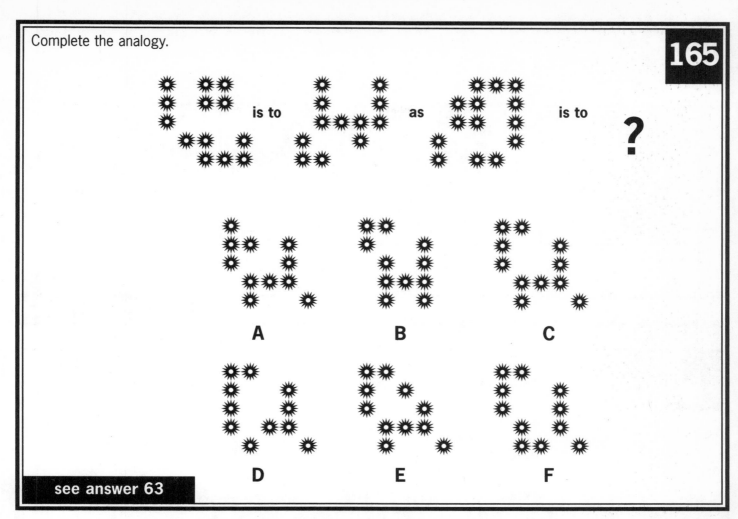

is to ... as ... is to ?

A   B   C

D   E   F

see answer 63

What comes next in this series?

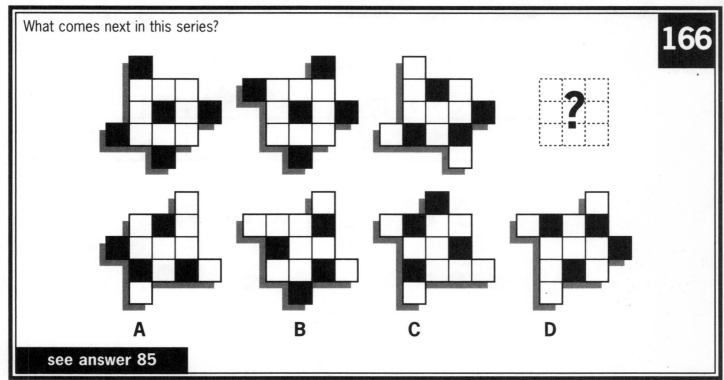

A   B   C   D

see answer 85

167

Which of the following is the odd one out?

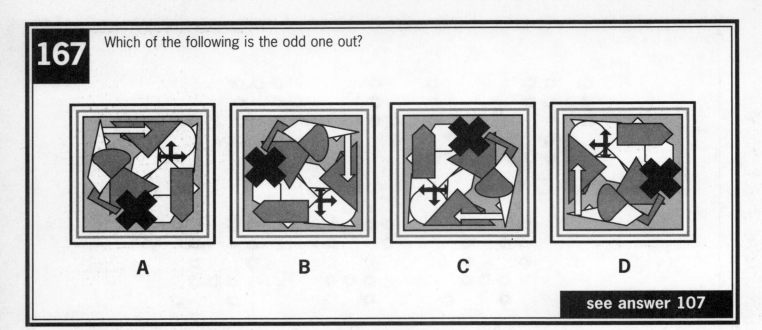

A   B   C   D

see answer 107

168

Each like symbol has the same value throughout. What is the missing symbol?
Clue: the small numbers are numbers carried when adding.

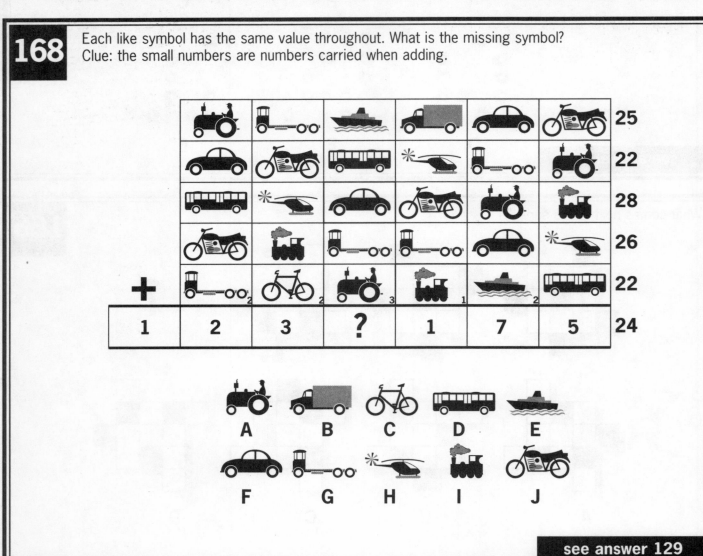

see answer 129

Find the 18 differences in picture B.

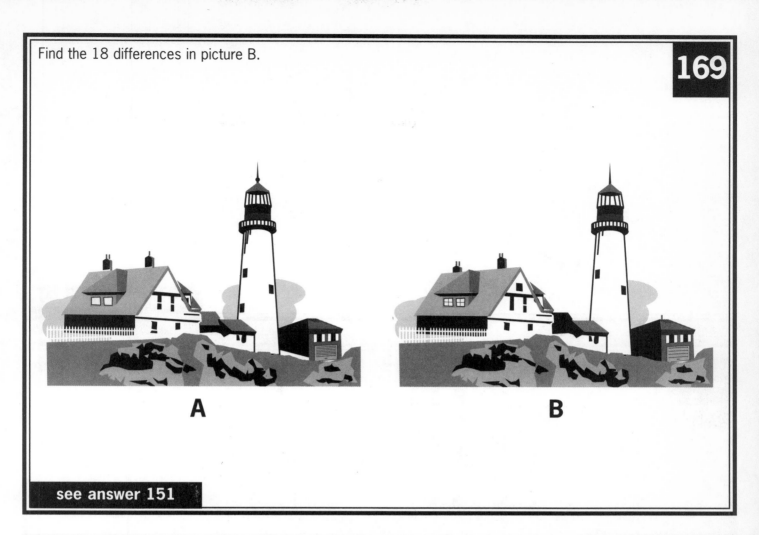

A

B

see answer 151

Which of the following is the odd one out?

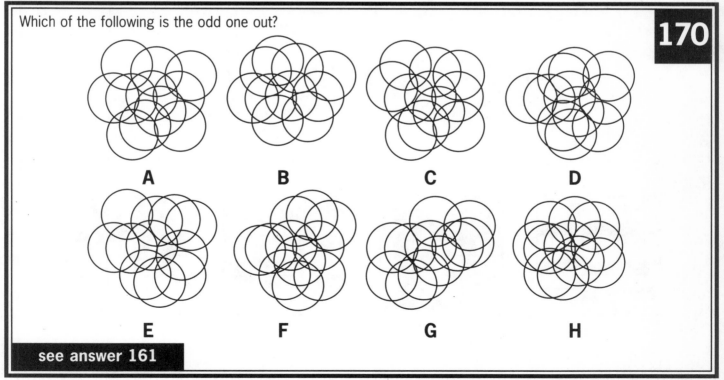

A   B   C   D

E   F   G   H

see answer 161

171

What should replace the question mark?

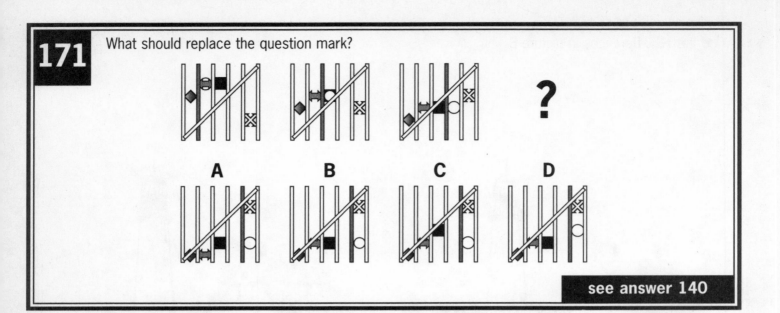

A   B   C   D

see answer 140

172

Complete the analogy.

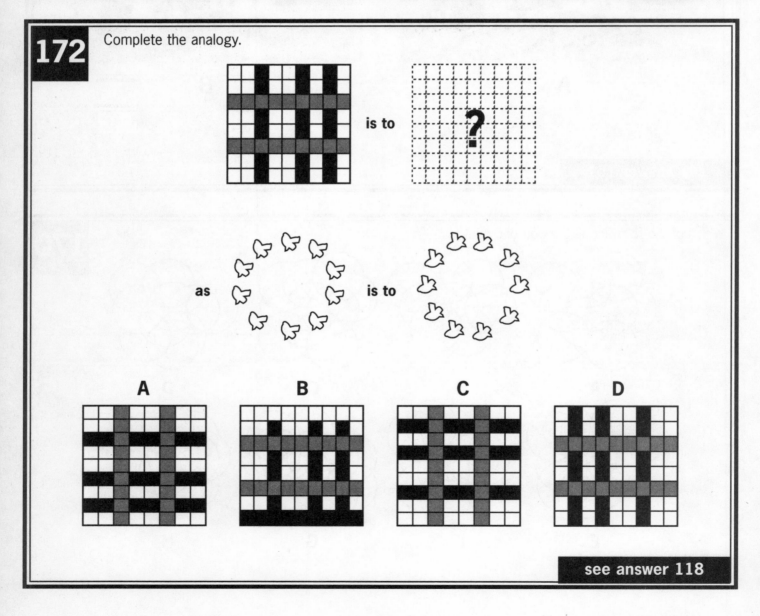

is to   ?

as   is to

A   B   C   D

see answer 118

Which path will the bomb take when released from this moving fighter-bomber on a calm day?

173

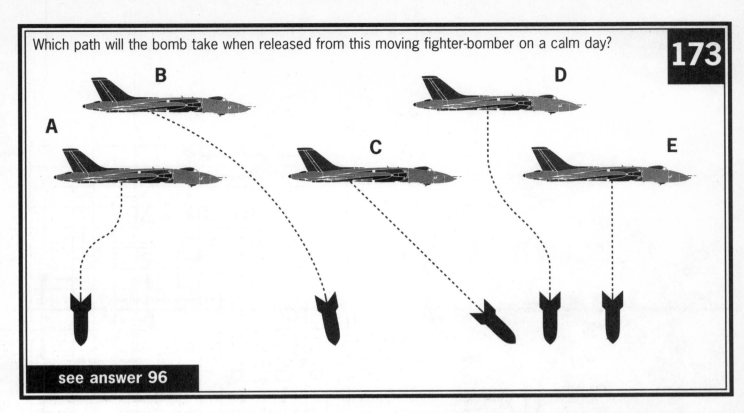

see answer 96

Which of the following is the odd one out?

174

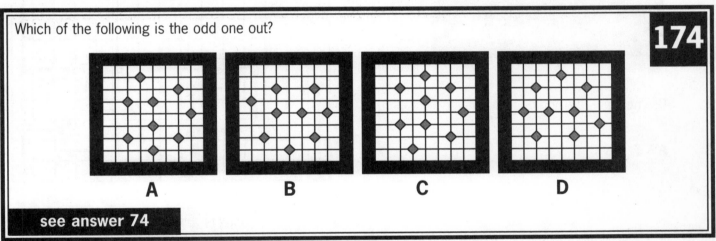

A   B   C   D

see answer 74

Which of the following is the odd one out?

175

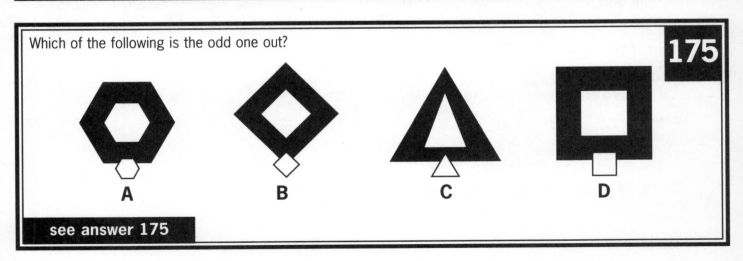

A   B   C   D

see answer 175

Answers

1

8

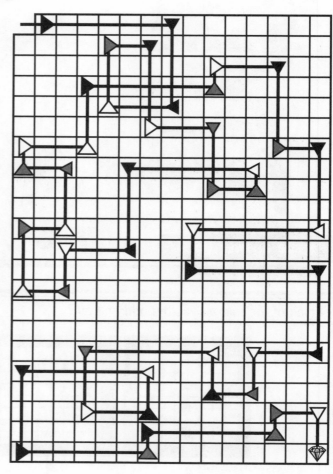

2   B. The black diamonds have changed position.

3   A & F, B & C, D & E.

4   D.

5   A. From what has gone before we can deduce that one ball goes over to the other side beore the next ball moves.

6   A. The analogous pattern is simply upside down.

7   A. The sequence is built according to the number of enclosed spaces in each shape.

9   E. The objects are rotating around the pole in a clockwise direction; the arrow must move next to make room for the cross to come round.

10   A.

11

13 The third on the second column and the fifth on the third column.

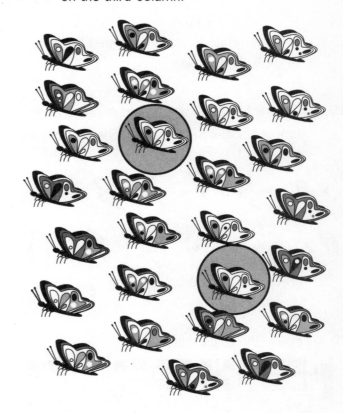

12 Here is proof that it can be done.

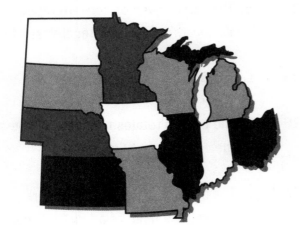

13 *See next column.*

14 A. The position of the balls is mirror reversed while the others are rotations of the same positions.

15 A. In all the others there are two pairs of two objects that touch each other.

16 C. The series of five foods always retains the same order: tomato, fruit, garlic, chicken, ice cream.

17 B. There are 3 changes.

Answers

18 C. The larger shape is condensed, the whole figure is horizontally and vertically flipped and the shading changes, respectively, from black to white, white to shaded, shaded to black and black/white to white/black.

19 The lightning bolt and the drum rotate an equal amount clockwise and anti- (counter) clockwise.

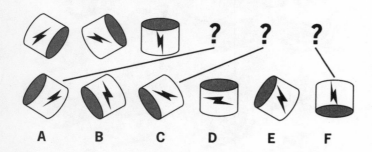

A B C D E F

20 Follow the black route.

21 A. At the end of the first ramp the ball will be moving vertically, and so will fall back down, eventually coming to rest at the lowest point.

22 B. It is a mirror image of the others.

23

24 B. The same seven objects are repeated continuously in each line, regardless of tone.

25 C. The figure flips onto its right side.

26 B. The pattern rotates two sunrays one step at a time.

27 C. The pattern rotates anti- (counter) clockwise, one tenth of a turn (36°) each step.

28 B. There is a block missing.

29 D.

30 B. The set is turned onto its right side and reflected horizontally.

31 D and G. The line in black is missing from both.

32 212 blocks (each set has 53).

33 A. The cog and star at the bottom have changed place.

34 B and F. In all others, the white circle is inside the smallest outer shape.

35 The 8 crossroads are marked

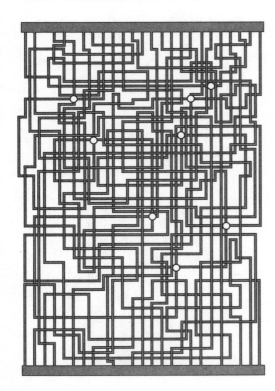

36

37 B. All the others have the same inner and outer shape.

38 *See next page.*

39

40 D. A black spot has changed position in the third row up.

Answers

38

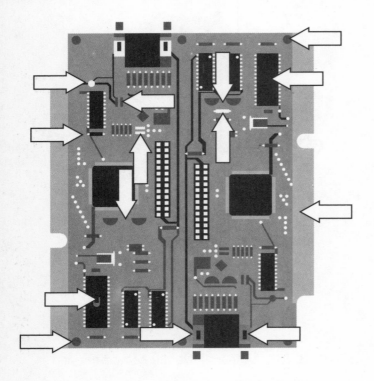

41 C and H. Both have one more white spot and one less black spot.

42 A will fall, B will move to the left.

43 A & B, C & D.

44 C and E. They are mirror images. The others are the same shape in different rotations.

45 D. Starting from the left in each row, the object rolls onto its right side with each move.

46 F. All the others have one or more difference.

47 D. The others are all rotated versions of the same figure on the top half, with the mirror-images on the bottom half, but the mirror-image of D is on top.

48 C. When the black arrows point down, the sequence begins with a black arrow.

49

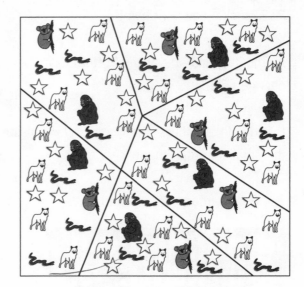

50

51

52 C. It is the only one where the arrow and block are not different shading in each rotation.

53 A & F.

54 C. It is a mirror image.

55 31 kangaroos.

56 *see next column*

57 B. The spots rotate clockwise one-fifth of a turn (72°) each time.

58 C. The pattern is made from continuously repeating the top row of tiles, rolling over two tiles with each row.

56 The missing symbol is G, the unladen truck (worth 0).

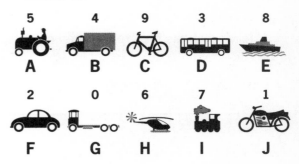

The values and working are as follows:

		4	9	5	3	1	
	×	2	8	6	7	0	
		3	4	6	7	1	7	0
	2	9	7	1	8	6	
	3	9	6	2	4	8	
	9	9	0	6	2		
1	4	2	0	0	5	3	7	7	0

59 B. Each object in the bottom row is a right-hand mirror-image of the shape above so, in this case, the image will be the same as the object.

60 D. The bottom white spot has changed place with the shaded spot now on its left.

61 C.

62 D. In the other sets the single black spot is in the reflection of the point of intersection of the two black line. Alternatively, in all the other cases is the single spot is superimposed on the other shape it would join a vertical or horizontal line of black spots.

Answers

63   B. Each two halves of the analogy, when put together, make a complete 5 x 5 square.

64   B. Billy's plot has the greatest perimeter.

65   There are eight differences.

66   D. The triangular shapes have switched position.

67   D. The inner shapes rotate anti-clockwise; the outer shapes rotate clockwise.

68   D.

69   A will rise, B will fall.

70   H. The inner squares have swapped shading; the bottom row is the top row taken as a whole and flipped upside down.

71   B and F.

72   D. Not all the shapes intersect.

73

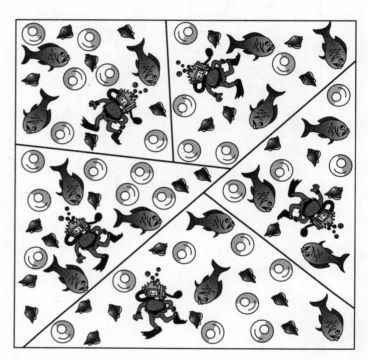

74   A. This is a mirror-image of the other shapes.

75   B. This is a mirror-image of the other shapes.

76   *see next page.*

77   D. The shape is turned on its right side and the shading is reversed.

78   C. The round spot and the rectangle have changed places.

76   157 bricks.

			1	2	3	4							
5	6	7	8	9	10	11	12	13	14				
	15	16	17	18	19	20	21	22	23	24	25		
26	27	28	29	30	31	32	33	34	35	36	37		
	38	39	40	41									
		42	43	44			45						
	46	47	48			49	50						
	51	52	53	54	55	56	57	58	59				
60	61	62	63	64	65	66	67	68	69	70			
71	72	73	74	75	76	77	78	79	80	81			
82	83	84	85	86	87	88	89	90	91	92	93		
	94	95	96	97	98	99	100	101	102	103	104		
	105	106	107	108	109	110	111	112	113	114			
	115				116								
	117		118		119	120	121		122	123	124		
125	126				127			128					
129	130		131			132		133	134				
135	136		137	138		139			140	141			
	142	143	144			145	146	147	148	149			
	150	151	152	153			154	155	156	157			

79   D. One of the balls has been displaced relative to the other sets, which are all rotated versions of the same set.

80   B. This is a mirror image of the other shapes, which are all rotated versions of the same object.

81   *see next column.*

82   *see next column.*

83   B. The sequence of arrows rotates anti-clockwise, and the diamond shape in the middle is the same shading as the arrow at the top.

84   A, If the rows were numbered down, the sequence would be 123, 312, 231.

81   Follow the black route.

82

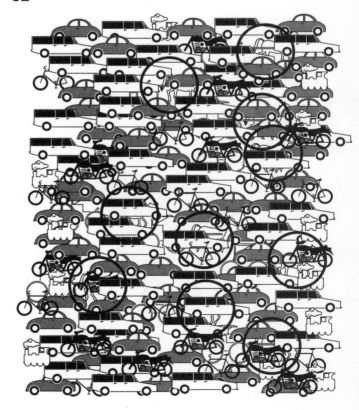

Answers

85 B. The second figure is a rotated mirror-image of the first, and so the missing figure is a similarly rotated mirror-image of the third figure.

86 B and C.

87 D. All the other spirals go anti- (counter) clockwise.

88 B. This is a mirror-image of the others.

89 C. Various blocks have been displaced in relation to the other shapes.

90 B. The sequence always adds two double-curved lines onto the end of the previous pattern, at the end of the last new point added.

91 C.

92 B.

93 H. The shape rotates one-eighth of a turn (45°) each time, but the leftmost star should be stacked below the one diagonally down to the right.

94 A. The values are:
leopard = 3;
flea = 2;
dog = 5;
rabbit = 4.
The sums are:
2 + 3 [5] = 5;
(4 + 4) − 2 [6] = 3 + 3 [6];
4 + 5 [9] = 3 + 3 + 3 [9];
the column sum is 3 + 2 + 3 + 5 [13] = dog + dog + flea (5 + 5 + 3 [13]).

95 C. This is a rotated mirror-image of the others.

96 B. The bomb will follow a smooth parabolic curve.

97 A. The pattern rolls vertically and horizontally, in steps of 4.

98 D. The others all go clockwise.

99 D and E. These are rotated mirror images of the other three.

100 E. The shapes rotate 72° clockwise each time.

101

102 C.

103 C.

104 C. The tree has an extra inner shape.

105 G. The black vertical stripes move one column to the right one stripe each time, rolling over as it reaches the end of the shape. The black horizontal stripe moves down one row each time.

106 B.

107 D. The arrow has come to the front of the objects below it.

108 It will drop.

109 D.

110 It will move apart.

111 13. Dove = 2; football = 3; earth = 5; spiral = 4.

112 C. Any cross in the middle three vertical tiles is always in the middle column, and the black spot is always in the same vertical column as in the tiles to the left and right of it.

113 The helicopter (worth 2).

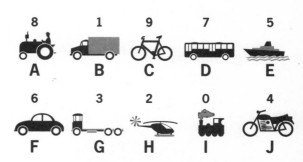

The symbols have the following values:

÷ 7	6	2	5	9	1	2
	8	9	4	1	6	

÷ 7	8	3	4	4	0
	1	1	9	2	0

3 6	2 0	1 2
− 3	− 8	− 2
3 3	1 2	1 0

Answers

114 Both will rise.

115 A.

116 A will rise, B will drop.

117 D.

118 C. The shapes are turned onto their left side.

119 D. The star is on the wrong side in relation to the other shapes.

120 C.

121 D.

122 F. The analogy is for two items to turn 180°, without shifting their position within the set.

123 E. The values are:

bear = 5,
horse = 1,
fish = 4,
bird = 3.

The sums are:

5 + 1 + 1 [7] = 4 + 3 [7];
3 + 3 [6] = 5 + 1 [6];
(4 − 1) [3] + 1 [4] = 3 + 1 [4].

The column is 4 + 5 + 3
[12 or fish + fish + fish].

124 A.

125 F. In all others the small ball is diagonally opposite to the two shaded spikes.

126 C. The objects are rotating one-sixth of a turn clockwise (60°) each step.

127 39 cobras.

128 B. The object flips onto its left side.

129 *see next page.*

130 14 spotted tiles.

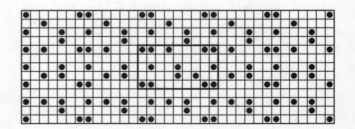

129 C. The bicycle (worth 0) is missing.

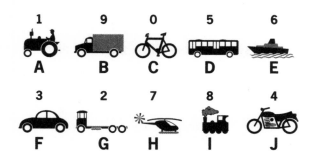

The values and working are as follows:

	1	2	6	9	3	4	25
	3	4	5	7	2	1	22
	5	7	3	4	1	8	28
	4	8	2	2	3	7	26
+	2	0	1	8	6	5	22
	1 7	3	0	1	7	5	24

130 *See previous page.*

131 E.

132 B. The black balls are mirror-reversed.

133 A. This is a rotated mirror-image of the other shapes.

134 C. All the others have in the middle, an enlarged version of the objects at top-left and bottom-right.

135

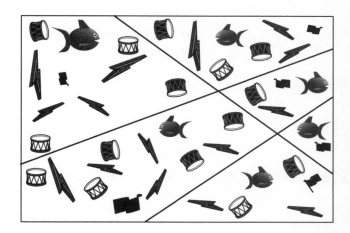

136 C. The internal configuration has changed hand in this shape).

137 C. The inner shapes rotate anti- (counter) clockwise; the outer shapes rotate clockwise.

138 H. The black columns of stars move to the right, as a pair, one column at a time; when a black column reaches the right edge, it returns to the left edge in the next set.

139 C. The same circles are rotated, except C, which are mirror images.

140 B.

141 C. The penguin's bill is slightly more open.

142 D.

Answers

143 C. The separate shaded cell is always one cell away from the group of three, and, if a corner group, is on the same vertical or horizontal line as the innermost cell of the group of three.

144 A.

145 17 rattlesnakes can be collected if you follow this route:

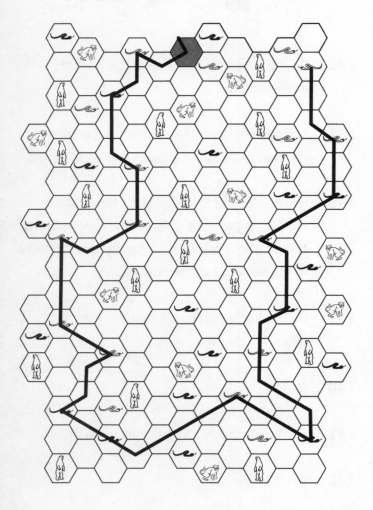

146 B. The pattern rolls to the left one step at a time.

147 The symbol is based on the number of shapes it appears in. For instance, the cone (bottom right) appears in two shapes, and the tube is in three.

148 B.

149 *See next page*

150 *See next page*

151 *See next page*

152 B. The balls on the diamond have switched places.

153 E. The jagged flower, top left in this set, is different to the jagged flowers in the others.

149

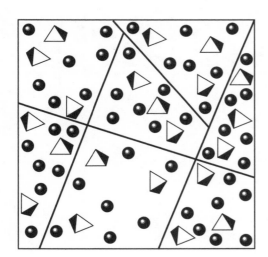

150

154 (a). They will reach the ground together (although they will be much further apart). As soon as the projectile is fired it is subject to gravity, and will approach the ground at the same downward speed as the brick, despite its forward motion.

151

155 It will rise.

156 B. The two sun symbols have reversed positions.

157 A. The lightning bold flips upside down and changes side, as in the analogous figure.

158 B

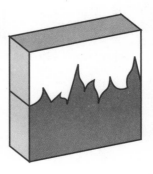

159 G. The line shown in black is missing.

160 E. The jet fighter is rolling to the left one fifth of a turn per step.

161 B. There are only 10 circles here, but in the others there are 11.

162 E. Fire is extinguised by a fire extinguisher as dirt is removed by a vacuum cleaner.

163 C. The lightning bolt and pointer shape have changed place at the bottom.

164 It will rise.

165 A and J. The loops have been distorted with respect to the others.

166 F. The figure has no eyebrows.

167 Both will fall.

168 C.

169 A will rise, B will drop.

170 D. The others are 90° rotations of the same pattern.

171 C. The angle between the hands remains the same, but in C the minute and hour hands are reversed.

172 Follow this string:

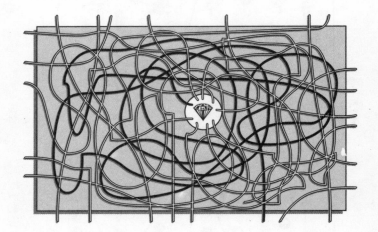

173 D.

174 B.

175 C.